ARROWHEAD

By Steve W

ISBN 9798628835296

About the Author

As a native of Brooklyn, New York, I spent my college years locally and graduated from Long Island University - Brooklyn campus - in 1971 with a B.A.

After graduation, I pursued a career as a commercial advertising photographer - 45 years - and had a world-class studio in the heart of the photography district in Manhattan.

Life, for me, was a journey uncharted. One of the many layovers was a place called Arrowhead. I hope you enjoy my story.

Dedications

I dedicate this book to all my friends from Arrowhead, Mike, Bernie, Whitey, Bobby, Paula, Pete, Bea, and Jerry.

Close in my heart, and with great affection, I hold the Zigg Zaggs: Alan, Ray, Ken, Arty, Bruce, and Anthony. Unfortunately, I don't have a photo of Anthony.

The original Zigg Zaggs, Steve, Ken, Ray, Alan

Bruce, Alan, Steve, Arty

Contents

Entered a Boy Exited a Man

Prologue

From 1966-74, on weekends and the summers, I worked at a Dude Ranch in upstate New York called Arrowhead. It was a unique place filled with drama, excitement, sex, and adventure, a microcosm of life. The rough-cut middle-class crowd it attracted was there to unwind, ride horses, find romance, and party all night. At 18 years old, I arrived with three simple goals: play Rock' n Roll, meet girls, and earn money.

Arrowhead

We practiced a few tunes while waiting for my brother Jeff and his friend Jerry to arrive with Bobby. It was November 1965, Bensonhurst, Brooklyn, and the Zigg Zagg's big audition for a steady weekend gig. Were we good enough to be the rock band at Arrowhead?

At 10 PM, the doorbell rang, and Alan looked out the window. "It's them," he shouted.

Jeff, Jerry, and Bobby were at the door, and our big moment had arrived.

As the trio walked in, to our amazement, the Arrowhead Dude Ranch representative was pie-eyed drunk. He reeked of booze and couldn't walk up the steps to our practice room without Jerry and Jeff holding him up.

"Steve, this is Bobby from Arrowhead. Where can he sit?" Jerry asked.

"He can sit here," Alan said as he grabbed a chair.

Jerry placed Bobby in his seat and propped him up. Bobby lit a cigar but couldn't keep his head upright.

"OK, boys, I'm ready," Bobby mumbled.

Was this the great music critic they sent? He could barely stay awake. We busted our balls for him?

Jeff looked at Bobby, then me, "OK, Steve, hit it," he said.

Bewildered, Ray, Alan, Eddy, and I looked at each other and paused. "OK, guys 1..2.. 3…4," I said.

We did our best version of Chuck Berry's *"You Can't Catch Me,"* finished, and looked over to our music critic.

Slumped in his chair, puffing a smelly cigar, Bobby mumbled with a slurred tongue, "Whath da hell do I know bout music? Yeah, ya got da job."

"When do we start, Bobby?" I asked

"I'll let ya know."

In the mid-60s to the early 70s, Dude Ranches - where single guys and gals could meet and mingle - were the rage. They were a place to get away for the weekend, ride horses, have sex, smoke pot, and play cowboy and cowgirl.

Arrowhead Dude Ranch was a convenient 90 miles from Manhattan in the Catskill Mountains, New York. It could accommodate 300 guests, had a stable of 60 horses, and several excellent riding instructors. Often, repeat guests - those who couldn't get enough of it - worked as waiters/waitresses in exchange for a free weekend.

The lounge was the focal point at night. It had a raised stage for live music, colored spotlights, a large bar with tables and chairs, and a sizable dance area. Everyone would congregate there to enjoy the evening and its festivities. In the winter, it was too cold to ride horses; Arrowhead doubled as a ski lodge.

More than a Dude Ranch, Arrowhead was a microcosm of life, complete with drama, intrigue, disappointment, triumph, and plenty of sex. It had all the ingredients of excitement that my friends and I could want.

A short time after our audition, Jeff spoke with the owner.

"Hi, Whitey, I heard Bobby gave his approval for my brother's Rock band."

"Yup. Tell him he can come and play for us."

"When do you want them?"

"Er, well, how about the second week of January?"

"OK, I'll tell him."

On a frigid Friday night in January, the Zigg Zaggs - crammed inside their car - were on NY Route 17 to Arrowhead Dude Ranch.

Alan, the oldest, had recently bought a used 1962 Oldsmobile 98. It was a huge car but barely had enough room to fit the four of us and all our equipment: a complete drum set, two big amplifiers, two guitar cases, microphone stands, and some clothing for the weekend.

Eddy and I sat in the back seat with the Fender amps and guitar cases. Alan and Ray sat in the front with our luggage, and the trunk was crammed with the drums. None of us could move an inch.

It was a 3-hour trip from Brooklyn to Arrowhead. We finally arrived at 9:30 PM with enough time to unpack our equipment, set up, and be ready to play for our 10 PM debut.

We slowly peeled ourselves out of the car and into the bitter minus 5-degree night. It was so cold and dry that the snow covering Arrowhead's lounge parking lot crackled when we walked on it, and our kneecaps shivered as we unloaded our equipment.

Taking my guitar from the backseat of Alan's car, I noticed the warm, welcoming glow of an amber neon sign flashing *Drink Miller Beer*. Relief from the bone-chilling cold was seconds away, and we worked quickly to get inside.

Before we left Brooklyn, I called Jerry.

"How many people would be at Arrowhead this weekend, Jerry?"

"During ski season, the Ranch usually has about 60-weekend guests." He replied.

"Oh, that's a good amount, Jerry."

"It's a long trip, Steve. Drive safely."

"I will, Jerry, thanks."

We expected a lively crowd, but the place was empty when I burst through the lounge door with my guitar. The only people inside were the bartender, one guest holding his drink, and a jukebox playing Country and Western music.

Whenever I made a big mistake in judgment, I'd get a sinking feeling in the pit of my stomach. As I entered, that feeling hit me, and my gut plunged.

Duh? Where were the crowds of boisterous, happy-to-see-the-Zigg Zagg people? I was shattered and embarrassed.

Not wanting the guys to know my true feelings, I took a deep breath and thought aloud, "No time to think, Steve. Just set up the instruments and ask questions later."

Readying our equipment and drums took only a few moments and was an excellent time to turn on the amps and tune-up. I was about to flip the switch when Alan cautioned,

"Don't turn on the amplifiers yet. The tubes need time to warm-up from the cold."

"OK, Let's get something to drink, boys," I replied.

We walked over to the bar, and I introduced myself to Mike, the bartender.

"Hi, my name is Steve. We're the rock band."

Mike was enormous. He stood 6 feet, 4 inches, and must have weighed 275 lbs. He had a scowl on his face, and I thought he would eat me for dinner.

"Oh, you're the band. Welcome to Arrowhead."

"Mike, it looks kinda empty. Where are all the guests?" I asked.

"Don't worry. People are still arriving. What are you have'n boys, drinks are on me."

We finished our drinks and quickly got back on the stage. Even after our first set - which lasted until 11:20 PM - there were only five half-awake people in the lounge.

It was not the big, loud crowd Jerry told me to expect. It was upsetting, but who cared? It's all there was.

Despite the lackluster turnout, we had an enjoyable time and played our music until 2 AM.

Still pumped from the alcohol, beer, and pot-smoking of the evening, none of us considered sleeping, so we grabbed our coats and ventured outside.

We walked around Arrowhead, oblivious to the bone-chilling minus 10 degrees. I looked up, "Wow, hey guys, look at this."

We were awestruck by the crystal clarity of the night sky and the millions of stars that peppered it. Except for the tiny spotlights illuminating the Arrowhead welcome sign, we were surrounded by pitch-blackness, dead silence, and the calm of the air. It was spooky and weird but oddly beautiful.

Blown away by the spectacle above, Ray lay flat on his back in the fresh snow to stare at the sky. We all followed. The only audible sounds were, "Wow." "Oh, man." "This is unreal." "What a trip." "This is heavy shit." We were stoned.

In the morning, I awoke earlier than the rest, showered, and went to the dining hall to eat. By 8:30 AM, the rest of the Zigg Zaggs stumbled out of bed, got dressed, and met me for our first meal of the day.

Breakfast at Arrowhead was served from 7:30 until 9 AM. Lunch was at 1:00 PM and dinner at 7:00 PM. None went hungry. Meals were excellent, ample, and the kitchen staff friendly.

We chatted with the weekend ski guests and finished our breakfast. Afterward, we hung out near the lobby fireplace, playing guitar and singing. It was a long while till our performance on Saturday night. So, after lunch, we spent the afternoon practicing but expected another dull evening.

A few more guests gathered in the lounge Saturday night - more people than we had on Friday - but hardly an improvement.

Disappointed in the turnout, I turned to Alan, "I don't think it's going to get any better than this."

"Yeah, Steve, there's barely anyone here."

Ray and Eddy nodded in agreement.

While we played our first song of the night, a cute blonde broke away from her dance partner and danced alone.

"Al," I said, "look at this one."

"She looks drunk, Steve."

"Yeah, she's probably going to fall on her face."

The blonde strutted on the dance floor - up and down, back and forth - and then removed her sweater. Our eyes bulged from our heads. For us 17-year old's, it was the most arousing thing we had ever seen.

"Steve, we got a live one," Ray shouted from behind the drums.

The few guests in the lounge and whatever staff behind the bar also noticed what she was doing and stopped talking. It was time to sparkle up the night.

"Hey guys," I said, "play *The Stripper*."

We switched gears from our usual Rock'n Roll and played that instrumental hoping she would take off more clothes. It worked.

She took off her bra. Then she removed her pants. There were cheers, whistles, and applause from everyone in the lounge.

Eddy shouted from the mic, "Take it off, honey; take it all off. The dull evening we anticipated had changed in a flash.

Just as it was getting hot and steamy, a man flew out from behind the bar. He ran to the tipsy blonde, covered her with a jacket, and ushered her out of the lounge. We were stunned.

"Oh man, that was the highlight of the night," I shouted. We were having fun and didn't understand why that guy covered her up.

Bobby was smoking his cigar and laughing as he approached us. "OK, boys, let's have some music," he told us.

"Why did he cover her up, Bobby?" I asked.

"Because we can lose our liquor license, Stevie."

The excitement was gone, and everything quieted down. We returned to our standard list of songs, and I began to laugh.

Alan asked, "What's so funny, Steve?"

"All of you complained that Arrowhead was an uptight place and didn't think we should come back. Do you still think it's uptight?"

Alan, Ray, and Eddy looked at me and said, "NO."

It was late Sunday morning and time to go back home to Brooklyn. I walked into the office to get paid where Whitey - he was called Whitey because he had blonde hair, blue eyes, and very fair skin - the owner of Arrowhead could be found.

"Whaddya think of the band, Whitey?" I asked.

"Well, uh, er, um, nobody seemed ta complain."

Nobody complained? That wasn't very encouraging. We had put our hearts and souls in this, and all he could say was, "Nobody complained."

He reached into his pocket and gave me the promised $200.

"Oh, can you fellers come back next week?"

"Yeah, OK," I quickly replied.

I reported back to the guys. They had already packed their stuff and our instruments and were ready to make the trek back home.

Alan asked anxiously, "Did you get paid, Steve? Are we coming back?"

I pulled the role of cash from my pocket.

"Here's $50 for you.. you…you… and $50 for me. They loved us. We're coming back next week."

Jody

When the Zigg Zaggs were at Arrowhead the previous weekend, it hardly had any guests. On our return trip, it had a lively crowd of 40 people. There were more skiers, and the action in the lounge was hot.

A petite, blue-eyed blonde with a drink in her hand was grooving to our music. Swaying and undulating, she stood apart from the other dancers. Who's that? I thought. I've got to meet her.

We finished our set, and I bolted over to Bernie - a riding instructor sitting at a table near the stage. He would know who that pretty blonde was and give me the scoop.

"Bernie, what's the story on that cute little blonde?"

"Oh, yeah. That's Jody. She's the little rich girl that comes here. Ya wanna meet her?"

"Yeah."

We walked from the table to the bar. Jody was sipping her drink and talking to some older guy.

"Who's the old geezer?" I asked Bernie.

"That's her cousin Tom. She tags along when he comes to Arrowhead."

Bernie introduced me, "Hey Jody, this is Steve,"

"Hi, Jody. I like the way you dance," I said with enthusiasm.

Unphased by my compliment, Jody looked at me but kept sipping her drink. I could see she wasn't a conversationalist, but she didn't turn away either. I was hopeful but knew it would be me doing all the talking.

Jody finished her drink and placed the empty glass on the bar.

"I'm still thirsty, Steve," she said, staring at me.

"Let me buy you another one," I replied

"What ya have'n, Jody?" Big Mike asked.

"7&7."

"Mike, two "7&7's," I replied.

"Yes, sir," Mike said, smiling.

Having a drink with me seemed a definite sign she was interested. We chatted for a while, and then I returned to the stage for the Zigg Zagg's last set of the night.

Jody danced with a few other guys during the final one hour of our set. Even Bernie made a move on her. I was jealous but could do nothing while still on the stage.

At 2:00 AM, the Zigg Zaggs were finished for the night and free to carouse.

After we packed up our instruments, I looked for Jody from the stage. She was sitting quietly at the bar, sipping her drink and alone.

"You still here?" I said in a friendly gesture.

"Yeah, I was waiting for you to finish." My heart pounded with excitement.

"Let's go to your room, Steve."

I couldn't believe my ears-what a bold statement. I hesitated.

"My room?" I asked.

"Yeah, don't they give you a room for the weekend?"

Oh, shit, I thought. How could I take Jody to my room when all the guys in the band are using it?

"Yes, but there's a problem."

"What?"

"I share it with the other guys in the band."

Was my big opportunity to get laid was over?

"Let's go upstairs," Jody said.

"To the lobby?"

"Yes, there's nobody there at this time."

"OK."

She took my hand, and we walked up the lounge steps to Arrowhead's lobby. It had a row of comfortable couches, a TV, and a fireplace. All that we needed to be comfortable. But, there was no privacy.

In the 1950s-60s, if you hadn't had sex by 15, you were a loser. Most of my friends were well versed in the sexual arts. At 17, and still a virgin, I didn't know jack about sex. To my friends, I talked the talk, but it was all façade. Now, with Jody, my moment had arrived.

At 2:30 AM, I expected to be alone in the lobby with Jody, and we would do our thing. It was not to be. Pete, Arrowhead's singing guitarist, was sitting on the couch trying to romance a girl he met at the bar.

Pete loudly greeted us as we walked in, "Hey, Stevie, what's doing?"

Jody and I sat on the couch near the TV, but I was embarrassed and made my reply short so that Pete would take the hint.

"Hey, Pete."

Fortunately for Jody and I, Pete wasn't having any luck. He nodded to us, smiled, and left the lobby with his girlfriend. The light was green.

Jody stretched on the couch, and I lay beside her. High with anticipation, I tried to unbutton her jeans, but she grabbed my hand abruptly and moved it away. I persisted.

Again, I attempted to undo her pants. She pushed my hand off her jeans.

"Aren't we having sex?" I asked.

Jody replied firmly, "No. Let's stay here and sleep."

Sleep? I didn't come here to sleep.

We tossed, turned, and spooned. I got on top of Jody; she got on top of me. We faced east, then west. I tried and tried, but no matter what, she wasn't interested in having sex.

Neither of us slept. At 6 AM and still dark, Jody got up from the couch, "Steve, I'm going home. Here's my phone number, call me." She put on her coat, got in her car, and drove home.

Frustrated and very tired, I quietly open the door to my room. All the guys were sleeping. I got into bed and quickly fell asleep.

In the winter months, Jody frequented Arrowhead. Sometimes she'd be with her cousin, and sometimes she was alone. When she was there, Jody was always cordial and friendly to me.

We danced, chatted, and had a good time. But whenever I attempted to get intimate, she would put me off. Finally, I got the message that it was not in my stars and gave up.

In early March, Jody entered the lounge alone. I had the urge - for a moment - to give it one more shot, but after calling, pursuing, and getting no response, I decided not to bother with her.

When the Zigg Zaggs went for our half-hour break, I slowly walked to the bar for a drink, but I ignored Jody this time. It was the smartest thing I did.

She saw me. I saw her. We nodded to each other in recognition, but that's all. Big Mike and I made some small talk, and I kept to myself.

From the corner of my eye, I noticed Jody walking towards me.

"Hi, Steve, I'm coming to Manhattan next weekend. I'm staying at the Broadway Hotel. Do you want to meet me? Here's the address."

Now she's handing me an invitation to meet her. Why the change of heart? I didn't know what to say and looked at the address she gave me.

"Next weekend?"

"Yeah, don't you want to meet me in Manhattan? I'll have a room, and you can show me the Big City."

I pretended to think about it - to get even with her - and maintained my blasé attitude for a few moments.

Jody looked angry with my non-response.

I quickly realized that too much hesitation would blow my big opportunity.

"OK. Yeah. See you next week."

Stuffing the paper in my pocket, I walked back to the stage, saying, "Hello, Manhattan. Goodbye, Virginity."

My tryst with Jody came at a convenient time. The Zigg Zaggs wouldn't be at Arrowhead, and I had some extra money to spend.

We planned to meet at 1 PM in front of the Broadway Hotel. I'd take her to some of the landmark places in Manhattan and buy lunch.

As I left my apartment to catch the subway to the city, the phone rang.

"Hello, Steve, it's Stuey. What are you doing today?"

"Hi, Stuey, I can't talk; I'm heading to Manhattan."

"What are you doing in Manhattan?"

"I tell you later."

At 1 PM, Jody was waiting in front of the hotel. She wore her Arrowhead lounge outfit - jeans, sneakers, tight sweater, and leather jacket, but this time she had on eye makeup and lipstick. Her attitude and appearance was a huge turnaround, surprising but sweet.

"Hi, Steve," Jody said as she gave me a big kiss on the cheek."

I came prepared for the day with $40, enough money to have lunch and do a little sight-seeing.

"Where are we going?" Jody asked

"The Empire State Building," I replied

She held my hand, and off we went.

It was a bright, sunny day as we entered the Empire State Building and took the elevator straight to the observation deck. The view was spectacular, and you could see for miles. Afterward, we had lunch at a local eatery and visited Macy's 34th Street flagship store. It, too, was a spectacle.

By 7 PM, we were hungry and ate at a restaurant further downtown, close to her hotel. When it was time to pay the check, Jody reached for it before I did.

"It's my turn to pay," Jody said.

She unfolded a wad of cash and paid the check. It was a good thing for me that Jody did. I had very little left from my $40.

The day was busy with all the walking and sightseeing, but there was only one thing on my mind.

"Jody, I'm tired. Let's go to your hotel."

The room was low-end: a single bed, TV, bathroom, a phone, and an alarm clock, probably the cheapest one in the hotel. But for us, it had everything we needed.

To relax and get in the mood, Jody turned on the TV. She undressed, got in the bed, and I followed. Jody lay on the right, with me on the left. We pulled the bedcover up to our necks and stared at the ceiling, naked and silent, waiting for something to happen. For a long 5 minutes, nothing did.

Then, Jody turned and looked at me. I realized that she wanted me to start the action. I reached for my pants and withdrew a Trojan from my pocket. Fumbling, I put it on, and we had sex.

There was no emotion, passion, or sound. We were two young adults performing a mechanical function.

The next morning was a beautiful day. The sun was shining, and we cuddled in bed. Everything was right. But at 7 AM, the phone rang.

Who the hell is that? It must be one of her stupid friends. What nerve. Calling us at 7 AM disturbing our peace. Jody answered.

"Hello?"

She handed me the phone, "It's your mother."

"MY MOTHER?'"

"Hello?"

"Steve, where are you? Why didn't you call and let me know where you were going? You've been gone all night. Your father and I were worried," my mother scolded.

How the fuck did she know where I was? Oh, that shithead, Stuey must have told her. Holy shit, my mother is on the phone, giving me a lecture. Whatever macho appeal I had with Jody was gone.

"Uh, Uh, OK, I'll be home soon."

My mother replied in a stern voice, "Well, I think you should be home right now."

"OK, OK."

I looked at Jody after hanging up the phone.

"Jody, I have to go. Will I see you at Arrowhead?"

"Yes."

I quickly got dressed, kissed her goodbye, and left the hotel room.

It was horrible. My masculinity was in the toilet, and I felt demoralized and humiliated by my mother.

As I rode the subway home, I thought about seeing Jody at Arrowhead. Perhaps I could redeem myself and regain my machismo? Maybe she would forget what had happened and we could be boyfriend and girlfriend?

Jody never returned, but one thing was sure, I wasn't a virgin anymore.

Official Arrowhead Band

In the winter, the Zigg Zaggs would gig at Arrowhead, depending on how many guests it had. When weekends were busy with 30 or more skiers, we made the trek. If there were less, we stayed home.

The arrangement suited us well. It put money in our pockets and allowed us to practice when we stayed home. With the money earned, we bought a much-needed PA system and paid Alan for the gas and oil changes on his 98 Oldsmobile.

We also added a bass player named Eddy. He was a few years younger than us and complained about being homesick when we stayed for the weekends. He left the band after a brief period of only two months.

Losing him created a hole in the band. To fill it, Alan quit playing rhythm guitar and picked up the bass. We were happy that he did. He turned out to be a great bassist. The other Eddy, a singer in the band, hated the winter. He dropped out and moved to Florida. Then, we found Ken.

Coming home from band practice, I noticed a mustachioed young man walking towards me in the street with a jaunty stride and a guitar case in hand. He stopped and looked at my guitar.

"You have a Gibson?" he asked.

"Yeah. I just bought a new 335. What's your name?"

"Ken."

"And yours?"

"Steve."

I immediately liked Ken.

"Do you want to jam?" I asked

"Yeah."

We walked upstairs to my apartment, and I plugged him into my Fender amp. We complimented each other and had fun for a half hour.

The Zigg Zaggs needed another guitar, and I knew Ken was the right person. We finished our jam session and put our guitars back in their cases.

"I have a band called the Zigg Zaggs and need another guitar. Would you be interested in joining?"

"Yeah."

"Oh, great. I'll tell the guys. Give me your phone number."

After Ken left, I felt a rush of adrenaline and quickly called Alan.

"Alan, I met a great guitar player named Ken. He'll make a terrific addition to the band."

"Yeah, we can use another guitar. When can we meet him?"

"I'll call and ask Ken to join us for a practice session."

"Did you tell Ray?" Alan asked.

"Not yet. I'll call him now."

Ken joined the band in the spring of 1966. He became a great asset and added many tunes to our repertoire. We also told him about our gig at Arrowhead. He was happy to join us.

On a guest-filled Memorial Day weekend, the Zigg Zaggs were working the crowd at Arrowhead. The music was hot, and the lounge had wall to wall people. Everyone was on fire for the 4-day holiday. Even Whitey was feeling good. And why not? He was racking in the bucks.

Late that Sunday, I went to the office to collect our $200.

"Hi, Whitey, can I get paid?"

Handing me the cash, "Hey Stefano," he asked, "How'd ya like to be the band for the rest of this summer?"

"You mean to play in the lounge during the week too?"

"Uh, er, not exactly."

"Then what?"

"Er, well, there's not enough people during the week for ya to play in the lounge."

"So, what would we do during the week?"

"Well, uh, you fellers can work in the kitchen during the week and be the band on the weekends."

The kitchen staff during the week and the band on the weekend? Humm. I pictured us playing on stage wearing food-stained white aprons and smelling of barbeque sauce. How do you get girls when you stink from food?

"OK, Whitey. I'll speak to the guys and let you know."

"Er, well, don't wait too long. I need an answer pretty soon."

Walking back to our room, I considered the upcoming summer and Whitey's proposal. It was tempting, but I didn't know he had an ulterior motive.

Working as the kitchen staff during the week and the rock band on the weekend, Whitey didn't have to hire any extra people. He'd save money on salaries by getting live music in the lounge and kitchen help.

The Zigg Zaggs had no other pressing engagements, and we could use the extra cash. I discussed it with the guys on the long ride home but withheld the part about working in the kitchen.

"Whitey asked me about working the entire summer at Arrowhead. What do you guys think?" There was a long silent pause. I looked at Alan.

"Sounds good to me, Steve."

"Ray?"

"I'm not sure, Steve. Let me think about it."

"Ken?"

"I don't know. Let me think about it."

Soon after my High School graduation in June 1966, the Zigg Zaggs traveled up Route 17 to Arrowhead for the entire summer.

We had a good deal. Whitey paid us an extra $50 a week for Ray, Alan, and me to work as kitchen staffers on weekdays. Ken had a part-time job in Brooklyn during the week and could come to Arrowhead only on weekends. The $200 for playing in the band on Friday and Saturday night still stood.

Alan and I loved the whole idea. We had a place to hang out in the hot, boring summer, meet girls, and make money. Ray was neutral about working at Arrowhead. He wasn't keen about working away from home for the entire summer and required a little friendly persuasion. Eventually, Ray agreed and came along with us. But there was a downside. Our room had issues.

the Attic

Guest accommodations at Arrowhead were simple. The rooms had a TV, a shower, heat, and the beds were reasonably comfortable. The walls were decorated with paper-thin wood paneling. If you farted or coughed, whoever was in the next room would hear it. You could describe the décor as 1960s funk. It was not the place to go if you wanted ambiance, elegant accommodations, or sumptuous dining.

The staff rooms were two notches below the guest rooms. All staffers, no matter what job they had at Arrowhead, were separate from the guests. Employees stayed in a seedy, two-floor bungalow with 4 rooms on each floor. On weekends, when Arrowhead was busy, kitchen staffers often shared their place with the other workers. We all got along, so we didn't mind.

The Zigg Zaggs had the worst accommodations. Whitey put us in the crooked, mold-ridden, dilapidated shack on the other side of the staff quarters, a leftover relic from the depression era.

Our room was a dump, merely a place to sleep, shower, and shave. It was riddled with holes in the walls and cracks in the windows that allowed the Catskill Mountains' beautiful fresh air to run through it. At night, we froze our buns no matter how many blankets we used.

After waking up every day freezing from the chilly night air and horrible backaches, I went to the office to ask Whitey if there was something he could do for us.

"Hi, Whitey. Can we get a nicer room?"

He laughingly said, "Er, well, what's wrong with whatch ya got?"

"Isn't there a room that doesn't have mold growing on the walls and in the bathroom?"

"Well, what about the attic?"

"The attic?"

"Come on. I'll show ya."

We walked to the second floor of the staff quarters, then to a door, opened it, and up another ten steps to the attic. The entrance wasn't full height but sized for a man of 5ft. 6 inches. Whitey opened that door, and we both bent down and entered. It was a surprisingly large area and room enough for a tall person.

"You can fit all your guitars and put 4 beds in here," Whitely said, smiling.

I looked around for a moment and thought the attic had great possibilities. But there were two big problems. Instead of sheetrock, a cardboard-like paneling with large holes covered the walls, and there wasn't any insulation. Like before, we would freeze from the chilly night air.

"If you fellers wanna fancy up the place, it's all yours," Whitely said.

"How do we do that?"

"I've got plenty of new sheetrock downstairs. You can remove the cardboard and put up new sheetrock, insulation and paint it."

Alan, Ray, and I used our downtime to work on our new room. We spent two days removing the cardboard wall covering, installing fiberglass insulation, and cutting and spackling the new sheetrock. On the third day, we painted. It was a big undertaking but worth it. The dirty, dingy unusable attic was now a palace and a unique room at Arrowhead.

Maintenance Men

The 4th of July weekend - Arrowhead's biggest - was around the corner. This year, Whitey expected 200 guests. It would be stressful for the staff, Zigg Zaggs, the riding instructors, everyone. With the pressure came problems.

While Ray, Alan, and I were doing a few chores, Whitey corralled the three of us for a talk. I suspected trouble.

"Mike and Bernie need an extra hand. Er, well, I need one of you fellers to work in the stables and two of you to work in the kitchen with me."

Working as a riding instructor was the macho job to have at Arrowhead, a guarantee to attract girls. I perked up when he said, "work in the stables."

"Which one of us works on the stables, Whitey?" I asked.

"Er well, I'll let Bernie and Mike decide."

For sure, they wouldn't pick Alan; he was 250lbs. So, it was either Ray or me.

Hoping to sweet talk Bernie and Mike, I walked up the parking lot hill to the barn promptly after lunch. To my surprise. Ray was already there talking and laughing with Mike.

Ah, ha. Now I knew why Ray wasn't with Alan and me at lunchtime.

"Steve, Mike, and Bernie asked me to work with the horses," Ray said, smiling."

I was so jealous but pretended not to be.

"Oh, that's great, Ray."

Shit. Ray would get all the girls, and I'd be washing dishes with Alan and smelling like meatloaf. Fuck!

After the big July holiday was over, Ray was the new riding instructor, and Alan and I were Arrowhead's shit kicker maintenance men.

Besides helping out in the kitchen on weekdays, Whitey had Alan and I mow the lawn, wash dishes, clean the pool, and tidy up the rifle range. I foolishly mentioned to Whitey that my father was a plumber. It was a mistake.

"Oh, Stefano, guest room 21 has a clogged toilet," Whitey said one time as he reached under the stainless-steel table in the kitchen. "Here's a plunger to unclog it." After that, when a toilet needed turd removal, my name was called.

Having the moniker of "toilet master" was not something I enjoyed. If word got out, it would make it impossible to attract women. Fortunately, female guests were unlikely to vacation at the Ranch during the week. Its clientele was mostly men in their late 20s to early 30s. Riding horses, drinking all night until they puked, and acting like pigs was their entertainment. They didn't care what job I had.

The weekends were different. Fridays through Sundays brought an average of 50 single girls that came to party. A jack-of-all-trades was my job during the week, but on the weekend, I was the sexy guitar player in the Zigg

Zaggs. The ladies had no clue about the dual role I had at Arrowhead, and that was OK with me.

On the second week at Arrowhead, Ray hooked up with Ann. She was a frequent guest and 10 years older than he was. On Friday and Saturday nights, she and Ray would meet in the lounge, then disappear. They acted like a submerging submarine; no one would see them again until they came up for air on Sunday. It was proof that working as a riding instructor was the sexiest job.

I was envious of Ray. He had a steady girlfriend and was a riding instructor. Try as I did, there was no romance for me in July, and it passed uneventfully. But the next month, there was hope.

It was the first weekend of August. Waiting for an early check-in was a cute, paper-thin petite brunette standing by the office - she reminded me of Jody but was a thinner version. I wanted a Coke from the vending machine, and as I passed by her, she smiled at me. I smiled back. It was encouraging.

On Friday evening, the Zigg Zaggs broke for 20 minutes, and the four of us walked to the bar. Sitting next to the "Drink Miller" neon sign, Ann patiently waited for Ray. Unexpectedly, right next to Ann was the gal that smiled at me earlier and her two girlfriends. Ray fell into the arms of his lovely, and I saw my opportunity.

"Hi, ladies, I'm Steve, this is Ken, this is Alan. What're your names?"

"I'm Cynthia, this is Francine, and this is Alice."

I moved closer to Alice. Ken and Alan talked with Cynthia and Francine.

"Hi, that was you at check-in?" I asked Alice.

"Yes, that was me."

"Is this your first time at Arrowhead?

"Yes. We came to ride horses and meet guys."

When she said, "meet guys," I knew my luck was changing.

"Well, you came to the right place."

I glanced at the bar clock and noticed our twenty-minute break was over.

"Excuse me, Alice. I have to get back and play. Will I see you later?"

"Maybe," she said with a snobbish tone.

By 2 AM, the lounge had thinned out, with only a few guests remaining. I looked for Alice, but she was gone. Ken was happy. He had no luck with Cynthia but found another cutie-pie to romance. Alan and I lit a joint and enjoyed the rest of the night.

The next day I dressed to get breakfast. Hoping to see Alice, I entered the dining room. She wasn't there, but her two friends were. I walked over to their table.

"Do you mind if I sit here?"

"No," Cynthia said.

"Where's your friend?" I asked.

"Alice?"

"Yeah."

"She didn't come with us. She's a late sleeper."

"Are you two going to make the first ride at 10?" I asked.

"Is that the time?" Francine asked.

"Yes. There are four rides on Saturday and Sunday. 2 in the morning and 2 in the afternoon."

"You know a lot about Arrowhead," Cynthia said with a smirk.

"Yes, I've been here many times."

Cynthia's condescending tone was a turnoff. I quickly ate my breakfast and left the table.

It was hot that weekend. Many guests gathered poolside to sunbathe and enjoy the water. When I stepped outside after breakfast, the noise and laughter from Arrowhead's pool were inviting. Instead of riding a horse, I went to my room, put my bathing suit on, and headed over to enjoy the fun.

As I got closer to the pool, a pencil-thin, petite female standing on the diving board was about to jump. When she hit the water, her body mass was so slight there wasn't a splash or disturbance, not even a ripple. It was Alice.

I found an empty pool chair and draped my towel over it. As I sat, Alice's head popped out from the water.

"Hi, Steve."

"Hey, Alice. I didn't see you in the dining room this morning."

"Yeah, I wasn't hungry, so I slept late. Steve, can you help me out of the water, please."

I reached over and pulled her up and out.

Alice was no more than 90lbs soaking wet. She wore a tiny red bikini - to be alluring, I supposed. On a physical level, she wasn't sexy, but she seemed interested in me, which was good enough.

"Is it OK if I sit with you, Steve?"

"Yeah, sure."

She dried herself off and laid flat on a chaise lounge, soaking up the sun.

"How long have you been playing in the band at Arrowhead, Steve?"

"A year."

"You only play at Arrowhead?"

"Just for the summer, but we also play for private parties."

"What do you do, Alice?"

"I'm a receptionist at a dentist's office."

"Where?"

"In Manhattan."

"You live in Manhattan?"

"No, Queens."

"Where do you live, Steve?"

"Brooklyn."

Just then, her two friends, Cynthia and Francine, appeared and broke into our conversation.

"We had a great ride, Alice. You should have come with us," Cynthia rudely interrupted.

"Francine, Cynthia, do you know Steve?" Alice asked her friends.

"Yes, we met last night and at breakfast this morning," Cynthia replied.

I didn't look at Cynthia or acknowledge her. She was on my shit list.

"Alice, Fran and I are going back to the room to shower and get ready for lunch," Cynthia said firmly. But she wasn't asking Alice. She was commanding her.

"OK, Cyn, I'll be right there."

Alice got up and asked, "Steve, will I see you later?"

"Yeah. See you later."

As the three left the pool, I quietly mumbled, "I know who's the boss in that bunch."

Promptly at 10 PM, Ken, Alan, Ray, and I began our Saturday night set. The lounge crowd was excited, and everyone appeared happy, dancing, and filled with drinks. When they were cheery and in a party mood, so were the Zigg Zaggs. We even caught a few whiffs of pot coming from the dance floor. It wasn't surprising. We were stoned too.

Dancing and grooving to our music were Cynthia, Francine, and Alice. All three had male dance partners. The girls smiled at me, and I greeted them with a nod. On our 11 PM break, I went outside to smoke a joint when I felt a tap on my shoulder.

"Hey, Steve, can I have some?"

I turned. It was Alice.

"Yeah, sure."

She had not one, but two giant drags.

"Where's your dance partner, Alice?"

"Oh, him? He's probably at the bar drinking."

"You get high, Alice?"

"Yeah, I'm from Queens, remember?"

Alice and I chatted for a while, enjoying the summer night when Alan appeared at the lounge door, "Steve, we're on."

"Alice, I gotta get back to work. Will I see you later?"

"Yeah."

Arrowhead's bar crowd had a predictable pattern. People trickled in at 9, the crowd volume peaked at 12, and slowly thinned until closing at 2:00 AM. If you wanted to be intimate with someone, pairing up between 11 - 12:30 PM was necessary. If you were still hanging out at the bar until 1:30 AM, alone, you weren't getting laid.

That night, the lounge had an active group, about 100 guests, and a handful of locals. When we ended our last set, there were only five people still at the bar. Alice said she would see me later, but she wasn't among the remaining bunch.

We put our equipment in a room behind the stage and locked the door.

"I'll see you guys later," I said.

"Where are you going?" asked Ken.

"I'm heading upstairs to the lobby. Maybe the chick that I smoked pot with is up there?"

"Steve, you're wasting time," Ken replied.

"Probably, Ken, but I'm gonna give it a shot."

I ran up the steps to the lobby only to find it empty. I paused and thought, Steve, it's 2:45 AM. You're a jerk.

Early Sunday morning, the Zigg Zaggs were still sleeping, and my curiosity about Alice woke me. I got dressed for breakfast and was in the dining room, hoping to see her. When I walked inside, neither she nor her friends, Francine and Cynthia, were there. But Bernie and Mike were.

"Good morning Steve," Mike said.

"Hi, Mike, Bernie."

Bernie, munching down a piece of French toast, mumbled, "I saw you hanging out with a skinny little thing last night. Did you get laid?"

Mike and Bernie chuckled at me. There were no subtleties with the Arrowhead riding instructors.

"No. All she did was smoke my pot."

"Steve, you have an image to uphold. Maybe she didn't like the weed you gave her? You must be slipping," Bernie said, laughing.

Mike and Bernie chuckled again. I didn't like it but was accustomed to their sarcasm.

"Yeah, I guess I'll have to try harder."

After lunch, I was rehearsing a few songs in the lobby when Alice walked in.

"Hi, Steve."

"Hi, Alice."

"I'm coming back in a few weeks. Will I see you then?"

Not wanting to let her know my true feelings, I hesitated, then replied, "Oh, yeah, Alice. I'll be here."

Just then, her friend Francine - while still holding the door - popped her head into the lobby.

"Alice. Cyn is in the car waiting for us."

Alice walked over to me and planted a big kiss on my lips.

"See you in a few weeks, Steve."

What was that? She ditches me for the night, then kisses me goodbye? Crazy.

Labor Day Weekend

The next three weeks were uneventful. Alan and I returned to our usual chores. Ray worked with Bernie and Mike, and Ken came up on the weekends to play in the band. The climax of the summer - the Labor Day weekend holiday - was fast approaching, and Whitey promised it would be another capacity crowd.

On the big weekend's first night, the Zigg Zaggs were playing *Summer in the City,* a favorite hit song of the time. The dancefloor was packed, and everyone was having a hot time. Eyeing the crowd, I unexpectedly found a familiar face. Alice was dancing and enjoying the music.

Until that moment, she was out of my thoughts, and I was enjoying my summer at Arrowhead. Seeing her again made me ambivalent. I wanted to like Alice but didn't trust her. Like before, she waved, I nodded.

"Hey, everyone," I shouted into the mic, "the band is taking a 20-minute break. We'll be back shortly."

We put our instruments aside, and the four of us walked to the bar for a drink.

"Whaddaya having boys? Drinks are on me," big Mike said.

We ordered and relaxed. I saw Alice on the opposite end of the bar with her friend Francine schmoozing with two guys. She noticed me and waved. I saw her and signaled back.

Sipping my Coke, I relaxed and didn't look in her direction. I chatted with the guys and listened to the Country and Western songs coming from the jukebox. Except for playing our music and the guests enjoying the evening, Alice and I made no contact until the following night.

Saturday evening and getting ready to play, I opened my guitar case when someone tapped me on the shoulder.

"Hi, Steve, how ya doing?"

I looked up. It was Alice.

"Hi, Alice. I'm doing good, and you?"

"Francine and I thought we would spend the Labor Day weekend at our favorite Dude Ranch."

"Oh, that's great, Alice. Glad you came up."

"Steve, can I speak with you later?"

I paused. What does she want now? Smoke my pot? Wish me a happy birthday? Get laid?

"Ah, yeah, OK. I'll be here."

"Good. See you later, Steve."

I looked at Ray, Alan, and Ken. They all had raised eyebrows. I shrugged my shoulders and said, "Hey, I have no idea what she wants."

A few people were still at the bar when we finished our set at 2:00 AM. Ann, waiting for Ray, was one of them. I looked around, but there was no Alice.

"I let that bitch pull my chain a second time. Steve, you're an ass," I said aloud.

"Hey, Steve. Alan and I are gonna smoke a joint by the lake. Wanna join us?" Ken asked.

"Yeah, Ken, that's a good idea. I'm gonna get a Coke. I'll meet you there."

I stepped off the stage and went upstairs to get a soda from the office vending machine.

Waiting for my Coke to drop, I heard footsteps on the second-floor stairway. I turned to look and saw Alice standing at the bottom of the steps.

"Hi, Steve, did you finish playing?"

"Yeah."

"What are you doing now?" Alice asked.

"Gonna drink my Coke."

"Do you want to come to my room?"

"Ah… yeah."

We walked upstairs to her room and sat on the bed.

"What about your friend Francine?" I asked.

"She's with some guy. Steve, I have something for both of us."

Alice opened the dresser drawer and pulled out two thick joints.

"I smoked your pot last time, now try mine," Alice said with a smile.

"This is potent shit, Alice," I said, taking a drag.

"Hey, it's from Queens. It's better than your Brooklyn weed."

Alice undressed, sat on the side of the bed, and kissed me. I didn't respond.

"What's wrong?" she asked.

Alice was flat-chested - more than I thought - and had hardly any feminine curves. Maybe it was the pot? Perhaps her lack of sexuality or a combination of both made me hesitate, but I was turned off. I never thought it possible with a naked girl sitting right next to me that this would happen.

It was decision time. What to do? Should I leave? Should I stay? Reality quickly confronted me. Steve, you haven't had sex for months. Stop thinking and take care of business. I took a breath, and my passion returned.

For the rest of the weekend, Alice and I hung out by the pool during the day and enjoyed each other's company at night. On Tuesday afternoon - the last day of the holiday - Alice and her friend Francine were leaving, and I met them in the parking lot to say goodbye.

"Alice, give me your number. I'll call you when I return home."

"When do you start college, Steve?"

"In two weeks."

"OK, call me."

"You guys have a safe trip home," I said, waving as they drove away.

From September to December, there was a lull in business at Arrowhead. Except for a handful of trigger-happy, beer-guzzling men wearing camouflage outfits for the hunting season, there were no guests. Hunters weren't interested in hearing the Zigg Zaggs' music.

Ken, Ray, Alan, and I packed our belongings and instruments then headed home to Brooklyn. For 4 months, we wouldn't be at the Ranch until the start of the ski season in January. Once I was settled in and back to college, I called Alice. We saw each other for a few months and even doubled dated, one time, with her friend Francine. Alice was fun, and I enjoyed her company, but I didn't hear from her after the new year, and we lost touch.

Apple Seed Pendant Necklace

The Zigg Zaggs had major problems after the summer of 1966. In January of 1967, Kenny became restless and left the band for other adventures. Ray lost interest in playing the drums, and he also quit. Losing them created a void, which had to be filled quickly.

After searching for replacements, my college buddy and friendly guitar procurer Mike introduced me to Bruce. Bruce was friendly, helpful, and had a knack for Country and Western music. Before he left the band, Kenny introduced us to Arty, a great drummer, to replace Ray. With these new members, we made exciting music.

Working at Arrowhead coincided with the tumult of the 1960s counterculture. The Vietnam War was raging, and drugs like pot, LSD, mescaline were fashionable. The other icons of that time, like tie-dye shirts, black lights, DayGlo paint, long hair, Peter Max posters, and astrology, were also hot items. The Zigg Zaggs, too, were a part of that turbulent time.

Along with our long hair, sideburns, and mustaches, we wore love beads, tie-dye shirts, and burned candles and incense on stage. Some of the staff at Arrowhead were years older than us and from the straight era of the 1940s. Getting high for them was attained the old-fashioned way by drinking large quantities of alcohol. Our "bent" attitude, pot-smoking, and 60s fashions put us at odds with a few employees. To them, we were aliens from another world, amusing but strange.

Arty, our new drummer, said the stage we played on was "the pits" and needed massive updating. He was right and suggested that we give it a makeover with black lights and DayGlo paint. I called Whitey to modernize and get the OK.

"Hi, Paula. It's Steve. Can I speak with Whitety?"

"Hi, Stevie. Yeah, he's right here."

"Hi, Whitey. We want to dress up the stage and modernize it with the new black lights and DayGlo paint. Whaddya think?"

"What's DayGlo paint?"

"It's the new craze, and it'll help add sparkle to the Arrowhead lounge and stage."

"Er well, OK, if you fellers want to fix it up, I'll pay for the lights and paint."

The next weekend we arrived early on Thursday and worked furiously to get the stage and hallway leading to the lounge ready for the weekend.

We hung black lights on the ceiling, painted the wall behind the stage and hallway to the lounge black, and decorated it with DayGlo Peter Max-style artwork. When we turned on the lights, the approach to the bar took on an unworldly look. It prepared everyone at the Ranch for the eclectic ensemble of psychedelic, Country and Western, blues, and pop music the Zigg Zaggs were about to unleash.

Each weekend, from January until the end of the ski season in 1967, we played at Arrowhead. The stage's new psychedelic look drew a hip crowd and heightened the Zigg Zaggs' reputation. All that extra work we did brought more revenue to the lounge's cash register.

Knowing this, I felt the Zigg Zaggs should also reap the benefits with a pay increase. But Whitey had difficulty talking about money, and it made him uneasy.

Instead, I would go to Arrowhead's new official manager, my old friend Bobby. Like Whitey, I knew where to find him.

Smoking his cigar, sharp and alert, Bobby looked over some paperwork when I knocked on the office door.

"Hi, Bobby, can we talk?"

"Hi, Stevie. What can I do for you?"

"I'd like to talk about money."

"OK."

"The Zigg Zaggs are packing them in at the lounge Friday and Saturday. There must be at least 200 people each evening. The cash register is getting stuffed with money, and we feel it's because of the band."

"Yeah, so?"

"Well, we'd like a raise."

"A raise?"

"Yeah. We've been making the same amount for two years, but the Ranch has been racking in the cash. What do you think?"

I had faith in Bobby. He was a reasonable person and on my side.

"OK, I'll speak to Whitey," Bobby replied, puffing his stogey and folding his arms.

I told the guys about my request for a pay increase. They approved, but two weekends passed with no raise. I called the Ranch.

"Hi Bobby, it's Steve. Did you speak with Whitey?"

"Oh, yeah, Stevie. When you come up this weekend, we'll talk."

Ambiguities like that were not a positive sign. We had no choice but to wait and see.

Fortunately, Whitey agreed. The original $200 payment would increase to $300. The guys were pleased with the new deal.

I dressed in a white turtleneck sweater, white-bleached jeans, and my new apple seed pendant necklace at Arrowhead that weekend. It was the Zigg Zagg's transcendental meditation phase. I looked like I spent time with the Beatles and their Maharishi from India. To celebrate our pay increase and get in the mood for Friday night, we smoked hashish.

After getting high with the guys, I slowly floated - like a feather - from our room upstairs, down the steps to the Arrowhead front office. At the same moment, checking in were two female guests.

Jill, a local high school gym teacher, and her friend Kate, an English teacher, turned to me. The three of us paused, but I stared at Jill.

Jill was attractive. She had dark blond hair, brown eyes, and an athletic figure. Kate, who I met previously, introduced us.

"Jill, this is Steve. He's in the band," Kate said.

Trying to be unconventional, I put both of my hands together and bowed in the same gesture as the Maharishi from India and said, "Greetings."

Jill looked utterly turned off and gave me the ice treatment. I quickly caught her drift.

"Well, ladies, I guess I'll see you later," I replied and glided down the hallway steps to the lounge.

Finishing our set, I noticed Jill sitting at the bar with two of Arrowhead's riding instructors. Hoping to re-engage her in a conversation, I approached.

Again, she ignored me and continued talking with her buddies.

Boy, I must be the invisible man.

I was disappointed, but only for a moment. Several other college girls were also at the bar. I did an about-face and eased my way towards them. They would appreciate my mustachioed, apple seed pendant necklace, Maharishi type persona.

"Hi, I'm Steve. Where are you girls from?"

"We're from the Bronx."

"I'm from Brooklyn. We're neighbors."

The summer of 67 was getting closer. The Zigg Zaggs faced a decision, work at Arrowhead during the week or on weekends? Alan and Arty were OK with playing there for the summer but could be there only on Friday night to Sunday morning. Bruce wasn't interested and left the band. Again, we had to replace a guitarist. Fortunately, we found Anthony.

As the only band member in college, summers were free for me, but I wouldn't work in the kitchen. I had to decide. Do I get a summer job and play with the Zigg Zaggs on weekends or work as a riding instructor during the week and play Friday and Saturday night?

The answer was easy. What could be better than spending the summer playing music, making money, meeting girls, and riding horses? Nothing.

the Only Sound I Heard

Ring, Ring.

"Hello?"

"Steve, it's Bernie. Jill, Kate, and I are going to Nathan's in Coney Island to eat hot dogs. We'll be in Brooklyn tomorrow. Do you want us to pick you up at your house?"

"Jill. Wow, I thought she didn't like me?" I asked Bernie.

"Steve, yes or no?"

"Yes, Bernie, yes."

"OK. See you later."

It was June 20, 1967. I stood on the corner of 13th street and Avenue K, Brooklyn, with my guitar and packed duffle bag waiting for Bernie, Jill, and Kate. I'd be working at Arrowhead for the entire summer.

The gang drove up in Jill's 64 Rambler.

The window rolled down, and Bernie enthusiastically said, "Hi, Steve."

"Hi, Bernie, Jill, Kate."

"Jill, are you and Kate going back to Arrowhead with Bernie and me?"

"No. We're going to my house in Bloomingburg. We'll eat dinner there, and then I'll drive you and Bernie to Arrowhead. OK?"

"That's OK with me. I'll save a bus ticket to upstate.

During the trip, we laughed and talked about Jill and Kate's experiences as new High School teachers and some of the funny things that Bernie and I did at Arrowhead. When we pulled up to Jill and Kate's house, we were tired and hungry.

Their house was a rental. Except for the two beds, one lamp, a couch, and a few pots and pans, there wasn't any other furniture. You could see they spent little time at home. It was a pitstop, a place only to sleep and rest.

"Kate, is there anything to eat? I'm starving," I asked.

"Yes, Steve. I have fresh chicken and broccoli in the fridge, but I can't cook. Can you?"

Fortunately, my mother taught me how to cook a few things, and chicken was one.

"Yeah, let me give it a shot."

Everyone wolfed down and enjoyed my cooking.

Jill jokingly said, "Steve, this chicken is good. Maybe you can cook for Kate and me?"

I was surprised by Jill's friendliness. When I tried to make small talk with her the first time we met, I got the ice treatment. She was a strange one.

"I'll pass on that offer, Jill. But let's keep it just between us four. I don't want anyone at Arrowhead to know about my cooking."

After a brief rest, the girls drove Bernie and me to Arrowhead. It was a 40-minute drive, north on Route 17, and a 2-mile trip on the twisting turning Cooley Road to

Arrowhead.

At night, the Ranch's single-lane road was unlit, dead quiet, and scary for those unfamiliar with it. As we approached, the only lights on the whole place were two spotlights illuminating the Arrowhead front lawn sign.

The girls drove up to the staff house. I opened the trunk of Jill's car and grabbed my guitar and duffle bag. Bernie got his things.

"See you guys next time," Jill said and drove away into the darkness.

"See you in the morning, Steve," Bernie said and walked into his room and closed the door.

"OK, Bernie, see you in the morning."

Alone, in the silence and dark of the night, I stood in front of the staff house. I wasn't ready to sleep. It was only 9:30 PM.

I never experienced the Ranch on the pre-summer weekdays. It differed completely from the busy action that I was expecting. There weren't any guests, music, festivities, or lights. Arrowhead was static, dead, and engulfed in pitch blackness. The only sound I heard were the crickets and frogs croaking from the lake behind the kitchen. It was spooky and creeped me out.

Is this what pre-summer looks like at Arrowhead? Things should be moving and shaking with loads of people. There's nobody here and nothing to do. Oh shit, what a mistake. I should never have come so soon. I slowly walked up to the attic, my new home for the next two and a half months.

While I unpacked and loaded an old chest of draws with my clothing, that familiar sinking feeling percolated in my stomach. I was filled with doubt and regret.

There wasn't anything else to do but get into bed. Hoping that things would improve and get livelier tomorrow, I pulled the cover over me and turned off the table light.

Oh, My Aching Ass

Early the next morning, I heard footsteps walking up to my attic room. Then, a knock on the door.

"Hey, Stefano. It's 6:30; time to get up."

"OK, Whitey, I'm getting up."

I showered, dressed, and walked up the hill to the stables, gung-ho and ready to start my first day on the job. Bernie and Mike were already there working.

"Hey, Steve. 60 horses are waiting to be curried, fed, watered, saddled, and readied for the day," Mike said in a stern voice.

"OK, Mike."

Every day at the stables, 7:00 AM till 7:00 PM, Mike Bernie and I worked, making it a grueling 12-hour day. My labors put me in super physical condition, but no one told me how much stuff there was to do. I was a candy-ass college student, unprepared, and inexperienced in the strenuous task of caring for horses. Boy, was I in for a rude awakening.

The first week was punishing. Each morning, after being let out for the evening, I opened the gate to let the horses return to the stables. They had to be brushed, fed a mixture of oats and corn, saddled, given hay, and watered. When all that was done, we tidied up and made the stables look nice and neat.

After those jobs were finished, whatever guests staying at the Ranch during the week, went riding. With only a few guests, the ride would last as long as three hours. When we had many, the ride was short.

Occasionally, we had several local folks - Hack Riders - that rode on a per-ride basis. Every so often, they'd show up, pay their fee at the office, and go riding. They were easy to please and demanded little.

Whitey also had a contract with a children's camp. Once a week, 10 to 15 campers would come to ride. They were an unruly wild bunch, and unlike the Hack Riders, it made the workload on the day they arrived, tedious.

Late in each day, when all the rides were over, the morning's chores were reversed; it was cleanup time. We'd feed the horses, stack their saddles, let the horses out for the night, rake the stables clear of horseshit, and lime the entire floor.

From the get-go, I left work every day, exhausted, and spent. My shoulders, thighs, feet, every muscle in my body ached. Walking up the steps to my attic room became an arduous and painful experience, and slowly, I would take my jeans and boots off to shower.

The big event was having dinner, and I looked forward to it. Sometimes I didn't have the energy to make it to the dining hall. The only thing that pushed me was my ravenous appetite.

At the end of the first week, I developed bleeding saddle sores and secretly had to change my underwear twice a day. Every ride reminded me of my soft cushy life. Oh, my aching ass.

Complaining to Bernie and Mike about the pain was worthless. They were tough guys and would probably laugh and give me no sympathy. How did Ray do it? He never complained or said a word. So, I kept my mouth shut, like Ray and persevered.

By the third week, there was a significant improvement. My saddle sores healed, and the muscle aches and pains that bothered me all those previous weeks disappeared. I even had the energy to stay awake past 8 PM. I endured. Despite it all, I gained 6lbs. My ordeal was over.

Yahoo! There is a God.

The second half of the summer was gone, and the hot month of August had arrived. Entering the lobby one afternoon, I noticed a man wearing a tie and jacket sitting at a makeshift desk in front of the office. It was odd. As I passed him, he looked up and called my name.

"Steve?"

"Yes?"

"Have a seat, Steve. I'd like to speak with you."

I sat in a chair and noticed Whitey, from his spot in the office, listening intently.

"Steve, how many hours do you work per day?"

"Ah, I'm in the stables at 7:00 AM and don't finish work until 7:00 PM."

"So, that's 12 hours?"

"Yes."

He wrote in his book.

"How many days do you work?"

"Six."

Again, he wrote.

"Do you like working at Arrowhead?"

"Yes."

"Do they treat you well?"

"Yes."

"What about your room?"

"What about it?"

"Well, is it clean? Do you have the proper toilet and shower facilities?"

"Yes."

"OK. Thanks for your help."

As I got up from my seat, Bernie and Mike came in, and they also sat down for questioning.

I went into the dining room to have lunch, and soon after, Bernie and Mike finished with the mystery man and sat next to me.

"What was that all about, Mike?"

"I'm not sure, Steve, but I know he was from the Labor Board. I think Whitey is not paying us what he should be paying."

Bernie laughed, "Yeah, he's never paid us what we're worth."

"What do you mean, Bernie."

"Steve, did you notice we never get tips?"

"Yeah, you're right. Nobody gives us tips."

"Well, Whitey charges the guests 15% extra for gratuities but keeps the money.".

"He does?"

"Yeah. He's been cheating us."

Two weeks later, I was in the office to collect my paycheck.

"Hi, Whitey. Can I get my pay?"

"Stefano, here's your money."

"Thank you."

I stuffed the pay envelope in my pocket and walked back to the stables. Bernie was fixing a saddle. He smiled and said, "Steve, did you look at your pay?"

"No."

"Go, look."

I opened the envelope and counted the cash. My pay went from 50 to 65 dollars per week.

"Bernie, I have 15 more dollars."

"Yeah, me too. Yahoo! There is a God," Bernie shouted.

Jack & Jill's

The workday was strenuous for everyone during the week, and after dinner, most staffers went straight to bed. Sometimes, Whitey showed a movie in the lounge or took the guests to Kilcoyne's, a local bar with a bartender that doubled as a magician. Otherwise, the nights were dull, and going to sleep at 9 PM or watching a flick was not what I considered a hot time. Having fun and meeting girls were my interests.

The little town where Arrowhead was located had a population of only 35. But in that itty-bitty town was Jack & Jill's luncheonette. It was open in the summer until midnight, and young female counselors from the surrounding summer camps congregated there after work. If Arrowhead had no action, Jack & Jill's would.

I had a driver's license but no car. Any traveling outside Arrowhead's property line depended on the availability of the Ranch's station wagon or a helpful, willing guest.

After dinner one evening, I knew the station wagon was free and asked Bernie if he wanted to go to Jack & Jill's for ice cream. It would be my first time there, and already, I was salivating, but it wasn't for the ice cream.

When we drove up to the parking area of Jack & Jill's, it was packed with 15 cars. When Bernie and I walked in, my head bounced left and right, ogling at the female counselors.

There were Blondes, Brunettes, even a Red-Head. Some girls were tall and lean, and others were short and well built. There was something for every man's taste.

Each booth had at least 4 to 6 girls busy chatting, eating ice cream, and having a grand time. For Bernie and me, Jack & Jill's was heaven in our tiny corner of the world.

"Bernie, why didn't you take me here sooner?"

"I wanted to surprise you, Steve."

All the booths were occupied, so we sat at the counter, and Bernie proudly introduced me to Jack and Jill.

"Steve, this is Jack and his wife, Jill. Steve is working with me at Arrowhead. He's from Brooklyn and plays in the band."

Jack was a cheerful, short round man with a charming demeanor and smile. Jill was his matched bookend. Jack wiped his hand on the white apron he was wearing and reached over the counter to shake mine.

"Please to meet you, Steve. Whatcha have'n?"

I looked up at the ice cream sundae menu above Jack's head.

"Ah… I'll have a hot fudge sundae with chocolate chip mint ice cream."

"Now there's a man that knows what he likes," Jerry said jokingly. "And you, Bernie?"

"I'll have the same, Jack."

While we devoured our evening treat, a waitress that worked there came out from inside the kitchen. Dana was pleasant looking, petite, and perky. She wasn't what you would call hot, nor was she frumpy, a girl right in the middle. The most significant asset she had was her high spirit and chattiness.

When Jack finished making my hot fudge sundae, Dana grabbed it out of his hands and placed it in front of me.

"High, my name is Dana. I hear you work at Arrowhead."

"Yup," I replied but was surprised that she already knew me.

We stared at each other for a few seconds.

Bernie and I finished our desserts, then said goodbye to Jack and Jill. As we walked out the door, I looked back to see Dana standing by the kitchen doorway, waving her hand and winking at me.

As we drove back to Arrowhead, Bernie turned, "Maybe you'll get laid tonight, Steve?"

"What do you mean, Bernie?"

Bernie replied with the grin of the Cheshire cat, "You'll see."

Tired from the day's activities, I got back to my room and promptly went to sleep.

I walked to the stables at 7:00 AM the next day. Bernie and Mike were saddling the horses when Bernie asked, "Hey, Steve'O. Did anything happen last night?"

"No, what was supposed to happen?"

"You'll see," Bernie said.

"Oh, OK. You and Mike are gonna keep me guessing?

Mike and Bernie looked at each other and laughed.

At 10 AM, we were saddling the guests for the first-morning ride when Dana parked her car and walked up the lot toward the stables. I helped a guest on his horse when Bernie signaled, "Hey, Steve'O, your girlfriend is here."

"My girlfriend?"

I didn't understand who he was talking about until I turned and saw Dana.

"Hi, Steve. I thought I'd go riding today. Got a horse for me?"

"Ah, yeah, Dana. I'll get one for you."

I went to the barn to get her a comfortable riding horse.

"Here, Dana, this one should be good for you."

"Can you help me with the horse, please?"

I put her left foot on the stirrup, gave her the reins, and pushed up on her butt.

"Thanks, Steve."

There were six people for my morning ride. With Dana, it was seven.

"OK, everyone, follow me," I shouted.

Leaving the corral, I looked back to see Bernie and Mike snickering. Why are they laughing?

I made the ride as exciting and fun-filled as possible. We rode across streams, thick patches of trees, and the Airplane field - a large open area where we could gallop for a long distance. The entire time we were on the ride, Dana was silent. She didn't engage me or speak with the other riders. It was strange.

When we got back to the stables, Dana dismounted.

"Thanks, Steve," were the only words she said.

Dana got into her car and drove away.

Bernie and Mike were excitedly waiting for me to tell them what happened as I brought her horse into the barn.

"What'd she say, Steve?" Bernie asked.

"Who are you talking about, Bernie?"

"Steve, you dummy, Dana."

"Oh, she didn't say anything the entire ride."

"No?" Bernie again laughed.

"Is this a private joke between you and Mike?"

"You'll see, Steve."

Every day that week, Dana came to ride. We repeated the same routine; She drove up at 9:30 AM, parked her car, I got her a horse, and she said nothing. Thursday night was different.

Bernie and I went to Jack and Jill's for our hot fudge sundae and to gawk at the female counselors. As usual, we sat at the counter. Jack was typically pleasant.

"Hey, boys, let me guess what you're having… hot fudge on chocolate chip mint ice cream?"

"That's right, Jack," I replied.

"Hey, Jack. Where's Dana? I don't see her," I asked.

"Oh, she went to get a few things, Steve. She'll be right back."

Bernie and I finished our treats and were about to leave when Dana walked in the front door carrying a few packages.

"Hi, Steve."

"Hi, Dana."

"Did you guys have your hot fudge sundaes?"

"Yes, we did. Are you riding with us tomorrow?"

"No, I have a lot of things to do. Maybe I'll see you next week?"

"OK, Dana, see you next week."

Bernie and I got up to leave.

"Good night, Jack, Jill. See you next week."

"OK, boys, see you next time," Jack replied.

We drove back to Arrowhead, parked in the lot, and walked back to the staff house.

"Good night, Bernie."

"See you in the morning, Steve."

I walked up the attic stairs, undressed, and went to sleep. Soon after, there was a soft knock on my door and a faint voice whispering, "Steve. It's Dana. Are you awake?"

When I didn't respond, the knock was more aggressive, and the voice a little louder.

"Steve, it's Dana. I'm ready. Don't you want me?"

I didn't respond. Now, the knock became a bang, and the voice shouted. "Steve, it's Dana. I'm ready for you. Don't you want me!"

What the hell was going on at my door? Still groggy from sleep, I wasn't sure and didn't answer.

Dana kept pounding, and finally, it woke me up. I stumbled to the door, opened it, and in burst Dana.

Putting her hands-on-hips, she demanded, "Well, you know what I'm here for."

"Huh…What?... No, I don't. What are you here for?" I replied.

To drive her point, she removed her clothes and plopped herself on my bed.

"I'm ready, Steve."

I got the message.

"OK, Dana, I'm ready too."

While we were screwing, she said the oddest thing.

"Penny for your thoughts, Steve."

"Dana, I'm thinking of only one thing."

"What's that?"

"Screwing you."

Ready for work the next morning, I slowly strolled up to the stables and happily thought about last night: the mysterious rendezvous with Dana, the manliness of the evening, and that I was so cool and such a stud.

When I walked inside, Bernie and Mike were laughing.

"Hey, Steve'O, bet you think you're so cool."

How did he know what I was thinking?

"What'd ya mean, Bernie?"

"You don't know, do ya?"

"Don't know what?"

"Steve, you dummy. Dana fucked every guy from here to Mexico. You're just another notch in her belt."

Mike and Bernie laughed with gusto.

"She has?" I replied.

The three of us burst into laughter. I didn't see Dana after that night.

Karma

As I prepared a few guests for the morning ride, a clip-clop, clip-clop sound came from the parking lot. A beautiful blaze-faced horse with a female rider was coming toward the stables.

"Who's that?" I asked Bernie.

"Oh, that's Karma. She lives a few miles down the road and comes to ride with us sometimes."

"She has a horse?"

"Oh, yeah. And it's a good one."

"Is she an experienced rider, Bernie?

"Yes, very."

"Introduce me."

Karma was petite, no more than 5ft 3, cute and shapely. Bernie and I walked over to her, and he presented me.

"Karma, this is Steve."

"Hi, Steve."

"Hi, Karma. Are you joining me on my ride?"

"Yes. Is that OK?"

"Of course."

"OK, everybody, follow me," I said to all my riders.

Instead of falling in line with the others, Karma rode boldly beside me to show everyone that she was special. Yes, I thought, especially stuck-up.

"So, can I ask you a question, Karma?"

"Yes?"

"How did you get that name? It has a unique meaning."

Looking not at me but straight ahead, she replied dismissively, "I prefer not to say."

"Oh. OK."

My hunch was right. Karma was a liberated girl of the 60s, but she was also snooty. I decided to test her skills.

Knowing my other riders were experienced, I quickly changed pace before moving off Cooley Road and onto our favorite horse path. I galloped up to a small hill and on to a narrow trail toward our first stop. All followed.

"Hey, Steve, you're going too fast," a rider complained.

"Hey Mike, I thought you wanted some excitement?"

He didn't reply, nor anyone else.

In a small clearing, we made the first stop. I dismounted and checked everyone's saddle to make sure it was tight and secure.

"Want me to check your saddle, Karma?"

"No. I'm good, Steve."

"Oh, OK."

After inspecting everyone's equipment, I got back on my horse and shouted, "I'm going to be moving fast. Anybody have a problem with that?" No one answered.

We ran most of the way, up and down hills, changing the pace often and making quick turns. All my riders were far behind, but amazingly, Karma was right next to me, on her horse, smiling.

The ride lasted about an hour. Everyone complained that it was way too rough and dirty, except for Karma. She was unscathed and had not a trace of mud anywhere. When we returned to the stables and dismounted, Karma politely grinned, "Thanks, Steve, nice try."

"Glad you liked the ride. See you next time."

I walked my horse to its stall and noticed Bernie was smirking.

"What's so funny, Bernie?"

"You tried to test her?"

"Yeah. I wanted to see how good she was."

"Steve, she's a better rider than any of us."

"OK, OK. Now I know."

The following week, Karma was back. She tied her horse to a post outside the stables and walked inside.

"Hello, is anybody here?" Karma yelled.

Bernie and Mike were out on errands, and I was alone. Hearing her call, I looked and saw her petite silhouette standing between the large open barn doors and the bright sun outside.

"Karma, is that you?"

"Hi, Steve. Can I come in?"

"Yeah, come in. What's up, Karma?"

"Do you need any help with the horses?"

I was surprised by her offer but couldn't turn it down.

"Yeah, I could use a little help putting on their bridles."

"Which ones need bridles?"

"The first through the fifth stall."

"OK."

Unsure if she could do the job correctly, I secretly watched her while I saddled a few horses in the back of the stables. When I finished, Karma was right behind me.

"Steve, they're done. What's next?"

"Hey, you're fast."

"Thank you," she replied

"There's a ride going out at 10, Karma. You wanna join us?"

"Yes. Let me water my horse."

"OK. I'll get my riders ready," I replied.

Bernie returned from his errands and noticed Karma on her horse, patiently waiting for the morning ride to start.

"I see your girlfriend is waiting for you, Steve," Bernie said.

"Whoa, Whoa. Hold on now, Bernie. First, she's not my girlfriend, and second, I have no interest in her."

"Steve has no interest in a good-looking girl. Yeah, sure."

"No, I'm serious."

"Steve, you dummy. You didn't notice she likes you?"

"Well, if she does, she's got a strange way of showing it, Bernie."

I slowly walked the horses with all my riders to the trail, and like before, Karma rode next to me.

It was a sunny, cloudless day. We trotted to a high spot in an open field where everyone could view the valley below. It was a spectacular sight. One rider shouted, "Steve, I smell bread."

We all paused, and everyone perked up to sniff the air.

"Oh, yeah," I said, "there's a bakery in the valley. Sometimes, when the wind is right, you can smell the fresh-baked bread from this spot."

Another rider asked, "Does this happen all the time, Steve?"

"Nope," I replied, "only when the conditions are right, and only when I take you."

Catching the smell of the bread made the ride unique and enjoyable. It put me in a good mood, and I didn't challenge anyone's riding skills.

On the returning leg of the ride, Karma seemed happy and very friendly. So, I asked again, "Now that we know each other better, how did you get the name Karma?"

"I'd rather not say just yet. I'll tell you later."

"OK. When you're ready, you'll let me know."

Humm… Making progress, I thought.

Sally Wants an Adventure

The following week at dinner, Bernie, Sally - our staff waitress - Mark - a guest - and I discussed cars. Mark boasted about the used WWll Jeep he just bought.

"Yeah, it's funky, but I like having 4-wheel drive. There's nothing I can't overcome with 4-wheel drive."

"How about taking the three of us for a ride, Mark?" I asked.

"Yeah, sure. Whenever you are ready."

"How about now?"

We all left the dining room, went outside to the parking lot, and Mark showed us his Jeep.

Mark's new toy was painted in camouflage green, had two seats in front, two in the back, a rollbar in the middle, and no creature comforts - no radio, heat, cushioning, nothing.

"So, guys, what do you think of my Jeep? Beautiful, isn't she?"

Bernie, Sally, and I looked at each other in silence.

There was barely enough room for the four of us, but for our purpose, it was the right car for a ride down an old country road.

"Hey, let's get in," I said.

We hoped in, and Mark started the engine.

"Where do you guys want to go?" Mark asked.

"How far does Cooley Road go, Bernie?" I asked.

"Many miles, Steve. It turns into a dirt road at some point."

"So, it's Cooley Road. Is everyone OK with that?" I asked.

Sally smiled, "Oh, so we'll have an adventure?"

"Mark, Sally wants an adventure," I stated.

"OK, Steve. An adventure for all of us," replied Mark.

We pulled out of the Arrowhead parking lot, turned left, and drove into the unknown.

There was some daylight when we started, but after two miles of travel, the sun went down, and the twilight covered us like a blanket. The only lights we had were from the Jeep's headlamps, which made Cooley Road spooky, but we didn't care. The balmy summer air, the moon, and the stars rushing past us were exciting and the only things that mattered.

Almost an hour went by, and the road seemed never-ending. Along the way, we saw a few houses scattered on either side. The farther we drove, the fewer homes we encountered, the more isolated we became. None of us gave it any thought. We were having a grand time.

Abruptly, the asphalt changed to dirt. The calm was over and replaced by a rough, crunchy noise. Now the ride was bumpy and unpleasant.

"Bernie, what happened to the electric polls?"

"There isn't any electricity out here, Steve."

After hearing that, Mark and Sally's expression went from happy to fearful.

"Steve, how much more should we go?" Mark asked.

"I thought you wanted an adventure, Mark?"

Bernie interrupted us, "Mark, drive a little more. I want Steve to see someone's house."

"A house? Who's house, Bernie?" I asked.

"A friend of yours, Steve."

"Who?"

"Karma."

"She lives down here?"

"Yes. Her father's a doctor. He spends his vacation time in their country home."

"Mark," Bernie ordered, "Turn left on this dirt driveway."

As he drove into Karma's long driveway, we could see a cabin about 200 ft. ahead, and on either side of us was a large open field of overgrown grass.

"Bernie, this is the sticks," I yelled.

"It sure is Steve."

"Why would anybody move out here?" I asked dismissively.

"For the peace and quiet?" Sally questioned.

"Peace and quiet? More like dead and forgotten," I answered.

Abruptly, we heard a loud bang, then a crack and a crunch. Mark hit something and veered into a ditch.

"What the fuck was that, Mark?" I asked.

"I don't know, Steve."

We all got out to assess the situation.

There was just enough light from the moon for us to see that the Jeep was in a ditch. It was a foot lower than the driveway, with a large rock blocking the left front wheel.

"Put the Jeep in reverse, Mark," Bernie commanded.

Mark tried to back out, but the Jeep kept spinning its wheels. While Mark hit the gas, the three of us pushed on the hood and bumper.

"1,2,3, push!" I yelled.

"Again, 1,2,3, push!"

We tried two more times with no luck.

"Mark, I thought you said the Jeep could get out of anything with 4-wheel drive?" I asked sarcastically.

"Looks like I was wrong, Steve."

"Bernie, go knock on Karma's door. Maybe she can help us?" I said.

"Me? She's your girlfriend, Steve. You go knock on her door."

I didn't want Karma to know I needed her help, but it wasn't the time to think of myself.

"Ah, OK."

I approached the cabin door and knocked.

"Hello, is anybody here? Karma? Hello?"

A few moments passed, and the door opened. Karma - in PJ's and a stunned look on her face - was standing with a lit kerosene lamp in hand, close to her face.

"Steve? What are you doing here?"

"Ah, we came to visit but got stuck in the ditch. Can you help us?"

She raised the lamp a little higher and looked out at Mark, Bernie, and Sally standing by the Jeep.

"No, I can't help you. My father is sleeping. I can't wake him. You'll have to leave."

"But we're stuck in the ditch. We need to call for help."

"There's no phone or electricity out here. You'll have to leave. I can't wake my father." She slammed the door in my face.

"That's what I get for being nice," I said and walked back to the group.

Mark nervously asked, "Whad she say, Steve?"

"You have to leave," I replied.

"That's what she said?" Bernie asked.

"Yeah, Bernie."

"I thought she was your girlfriend, Steve?" Sally asked.

"Sally, she's not my GIRLFRIEND!"

"Bernie, how far back is Arrowhead?" I asked.

"I'm not sure. Maybe 15 miles?"

Fortunately, it was a 3/4 moon. The stars were shining. The crickets were chirping. It was a perfect night for a walking trek back to Arrowhead.

I threw my hands in the air, "Well, everyone, let's start walking."

So, we walked and walked and walked.

The light from the moon helped us see the road, but just in case something went wrong, we huddled close to each other. A long while passed before the dirt changed to asphalt. Still, there weren't any signs of civilization; no houses, no phones, no electricity, just crickets, frogs, and mosquitos.

"Bernie, when do we see lights?" Sally asked with a nervous voice.

"Sally, keep going. We're getting close."

"But what about my Jeep?" Mark asked.

"Don't worry, Mark. Karma won't steal your Jeep." I replied.

"It is easy for you to say, Steve. It's not your car that's stuck."

We kept walking.

"Hey, I see a light!" Sally shouted and pointed.

As we approached, the tiny glimmer grew brighter, and we could just about see the outline of a house. Not only were the lights on inside, but there was a telephone pole next to it.

Bernie bravely went to the door and knocked while we stayed on the road. More lights went on in the house, and a man opened the door.

"Yes?"

"Excuse me. Our Jeep got stuck in the road some ways back. Can I use your phone to get help?"

A few minutes later, Bernie came out of the house.

"I spoke with Morty," Bernie said, "he'll be here soon to pick us up."

At breakfast the next day, our adventure was the hot topic of the morning. Bernie, Sally, Mark, Morty, Whitey,

Mike, and the guests staying for the week gathered to hear the details.

"Whitey, how far does Cooley road go?" I asked

"Ah, well, I think it goes all the way to Kingston?"

"That far?"

"Yep, Stefano, but there are no lights, just a dirt road."

"What demon possessed you to drive to such a remote spot, Steve?" Morty asked.

"I wanted to see the girl with the blaze face horse. Bernie told me she lived out there."

"You mean you wanted to get laid?"

His crude statement angered me.

"No, Morty! I'm not interested."

"Yeah, sure, Stevie."

"No, I'm not. When Karma came out to see who was knocking on the door, she told me to get lost."

"Steve's right Morty. She wasn't interested in helping us," Bernies said.

I stuck my tongue out at Morty.

After the Jeep incident, we didn't see Karma at Arrowhead. She didn't ride or help us at the stables.

Early on a Monday morning - my day off - I heard footsteps walking up to my door.

Knock, Knock.

"Steve, it's Bernie. There's someone that wants to see you and say goodbye."

"Who wants to see me?"

I heard a familiar voice, "Me."

"Karma?"

"Steve, can I come in?"

"Yeah. Just a minute. Let me put on my pants."

I opened the door to let her in.

"Hey, Karma. What's up?"

"Hi, Steve. I was going home for the rest of the summer and came to say goodbye."

"Oh? Where's home?"

"Rockaway."

"Queens?"

"Yup."

We smiled. But it was an awkward moment.

"Steve, I want to apologize."

"Apologize for what?"

"For not being nice to you when you knocked on my cabin door for help."

"Oh, that? Hey, I forgot all about it, Karma."

"Well, I'd like to see you after the summer when you get home. Here's my phone number. Promise me you'll call."

I was taken aback by her request. Secretly, I was interested in Karma, but she was so self-important and uninterested in me every time we were together.

"Sure. I'll call."

"Goodbye," she said as she kissed me on the cheek. "See you later, Steve."

It was a sweet moment.

Waiting on Cooley road was her father in a chauffeured limousine. I watched from my attic room window as she got in the car and drove away.

I looked at the paper with the phone number. Yes. I'll call and discover how she got that name.

Guitar Playing Singing Hippie

Bernie and I became close friends in the summer of 1968. He taught me how to use a lasso, be an excellent riding instructor, and a few things about horses' biology and structure.

Bernie was always supportive of the Zigg Zaggs and would dance and groove to our music every Friday and Saturday night. He was three years older than I was, yet we shared the same love for spontaneity, excitement, and adventure.

In the long summer evenings, after work, we made our usual stop at Jack and Jill's but often drove the twisting Catskill Mt. roads, cruising the local bars looking for what we loved most, girls.

We never had conflicts; our taste in women was the opposite. He liked the thin skinny types. I preferred them voluptuous and fleshy.

Every weekend at Arrowhead brought an eclectic mix of girls. There were tall ones, short ones, thin and plump. Some were buxom and sexy, and some were flat-chested and frumpy. It was always a fantastic buffet from which to choose.

Yes, the girls were there to have fun, ride horses, party, drink, and enjoy a weekend in upstate New York. But secretly, they were there to meet men. And the guys were there to connect with the girls. It was a mutually compatible group.

During the week, I was the hard riding leather-wearing macho man cowboy, and on the weekend, the soothing guitar playing singing hippie. For a boy of 20, it was the most exciting place to work.

The big 4th of July holiday fell on a Tuesday, making it a four-day weekend. Although the Ranch was at full capacity, Whitey was worried. Most of the guests were females. He gathered all the men staffers to the stables and gave us a pep talk.

"Er, um, well. You guys are gonna have to help me out. 200 single girls are gonna be here this 4th of July, and ya better be friendly to them."

After Whitey finished his speech and was a reasonable distance away, Bernie and I looked at each other in amazement and simultaneously yelled, "Holy Shit, 200 girls! Yahoo!"

Completing my Friday chores, I quickly dressed, hurried to the dining hall for dinner, and gobbled down my food. Next, I ran to the lounge, readied the band equipment, and positioned myself at the bar waiting for Whitey's bounty of beauties to arrive. Bernie joined me. We ordered two Cokes and waited.

By 9:30 PM, the soft parade began. Starting from check-in at the front desk, the DayGlo lighted hallway and the long walk to the lounge came the 200. A few entered as singles. Others came as a group, but most of them arrived with a female friend.

The mixture of girls was so varied that Bernie's head and mine needed to be screwed back on our shoulders from turning left and right so much.

"Oh, Wow."

"Oooh."

"Ahhh."

"Ugh," were the quiet sounds Bernie and I voiced as they marched in and gathered at the bar. Neither of us felt the need to make any quick decisions on who to approach. The evening was young, and Whitey's promise was correct.

Glancing at the bar clock and noticing the time, I snapped out of my quiet euphoria and briskly walked back to the stage.

We played our Zigg Zagg's opening repertoire and got everyone in the mood to party. While performing our set, I noticed a very shapely blonde swaying to the music in front of the dance floor.

She looked different from all the other girls with her Mia Farrow hairstyle, tight jeans, white sneakers, and fancy belt.

When we finished our set, I looked for the pretty blonde in the crowded lounge, but the glare from the stage lights and thick cigarette smoke made it impossible to tell where she went. I had to find her.

"Hey, guys, I'm gonna get a drink. See you in twenty minutes."

Twisting my way through the congestion of warm bodies, I found the blonde sitting on a barstool next to her female friend. She was a knockout and up close, looked even better than she did on the dance floor. But I wasn't her only admirer.

Over the blaring music of the Juke Box, a guy was hovering over her and talking non-stop. How am I going to introduce myself with this bozo laying his rap on her?

Getting a soda would be wise, but there wasn't an open space for me to fit at the bar, so I waited. A spot opened unexpectedly three seats from the blonde, and I rushed to fill it. I signaled to the bartender for a drink.

"What are ya having, Stevie?" she asked.

"Ah, give me a Rum and Coke, Bea."

Waiting for my soda, I listened and watched Mr. Slick deliver his loud, aggressive rap. The blonde and her friend kept sipping their drinks, looking at him without expression and unimpressed. Finally, he stopped talking and walked away. My opportunity arrived.

"Hi, I'm Steve. What's your name?" I said to the blonde.

Nursing her drink through a skinny straw, she looked at me, kept drinking, but didn't reply.

A few moments passed. Blondie slowly put her glass on the counter and, at last, replied, "Justine."

Her girlfriend quickly followed, "Hi, I'm Carol."

Not to be rude, I looked at both, "Is this your first time at a Dude Ranch?"

Justine was silent, but Carol replied enthusiastically, "Yes."

Then, the flood gates opened. Carol began a catalog of information - where she and Justine lived - where they worked and what they did on their jobs. I was hoping Justine would say something, anything, but no. Her friend continued the conversation nonstop.

I liked Carol's energy but thought her too skinny. Justine was my type but didn't speak. What to do?

Carol finally stopped talking. I was about to engage with Justine when I looked at the clock. It was time to get back on stage. Getting to know her would have to wait.

"Ladies, I must get back to work."

The Zigg Zaggs played until 2 AM. Often, I'd look down from the stage to see Justine dancing. Unfortunately for me, she had six guys hitting on her throughout the night. It wasn't surprising. She was the best-looking girl at Arrowhead, and my chance of scoring with her was a big fat zero.

As I left the stage, Arty smiled, "Steve, there should be plenty of choices for you tonight."

"I'm not so sure. The one I was interested in is gone."

"What about you, Arty?"

"Oh, I found someone earlier. She told me to meet her in the lobby," Arty replied.

"OK, good luck."

"Hey, I'll see you guys later," I shouted, jumping off the stage, "I'm gonna get a drink."

Justine was gone, and I went to the bar and ordered a Coke to drown my sorrows. While having my pity-me-drink, a hand touched my left shoulder. I turned to see who it was. With a drink in hand, it was Justine.

"Is that the same one you've been nursing all night?" I asked.

"No, it's number 5.

"I see you were having a good time tonight," I said.

"Yeah. It was fun dancing to the music."

"You're a very popular girl."

"Thank you."

"So, what are we going to do?" Justine asked.

"I don't know. What did you have in mind?" I asked.

"Let's go to my room."

I was blown away and almost fell off my bar stool. A few moments passed before I replied.

"Yes."

We walked to her room, but when Justine struggled to put the key in the door lock, I realized she was soused.

"Let me do that, Justine."

I opened the door to an empty room.

"Ah, where's your friend Carol?"

"She met some guy. Steve, sit on the bed while I put something on."

Justine went into the bathroom and closed the door. I sat back on the bed, put my hands behind my head, and relaxed. About 10 minutes passed without her coming out. I got worried.

"Justine, are you OK?"

The door opened. Silhouetted by the bathroom light behind her and wearing only a see-through black negligee,

Justine posed with one hand on hip and the other on the door frame. My jaw dropped.

With her thin waist, large breasts, and wide hips, Justine's curvy figure was dazzling. She looked like a Playboy centerfold.

"Steve, do you like it?"

My heart pounded, and my blood pressure shot up.

"Yes, I do."

"Good, I'm all yours."

Macho Man Cowboy

Wasted from the hoopla of the night, I crawled back to my room around 5 AM and got a little sleep. My rest was short-lived, and I awoke at 7 AM and went for an early breakfast.

The dining hall was bustling with female guests. Some I saw Friday night, but it also had ones I didn't. All were a lively crew munching and enjoying their morning meal.

There was an open seat at a table of five girls. I quickly grabbed it and introduced myself.

"Hi, I'm Steve. What're your names?"

"I'm Susan; this is Ann, Margie, Jackie, Roberta."

"You're in the band," Susan said.

"Uh-huh."

"What time is the first ride, Steve?" asked Roberta.

"The first ride is always 10 AM."

Susan picked up her coffee cup, "I was told Arrowhead has the best horses of all the Dude Ranches."

"Yes, it does. You're all going riding this morning?" I asked.

"You ride horses too?" Susan remarked.

I caught the drift of her mocking question and wanted to say, "Oh, you snotty bitch, fuck you," but held my tongue.

Having breakfast with the girls was fun, but my thoughts were on Justine. Often, I glanced around to look for her, hoping she would make it for breakfast. She never did.

I grew tired of the small talk with the girls at the table, finished eating, and remarked, "I guess I'll see you all on the morning ride?" and left the dining room.

The first ride of Saturday morning was always hectic and had the largest crowd of gung-ho guests. Most were first-time riders and quietly waited their turn for Bernie and Mike to get them a horse. Others were impatient, and some were demanding and rude.

When I approached the stables, Bernie asked, "Hey Steve'O, we need help. Can you take out the novice ride?"

Bernie was always helpful to me. I couldn't refuse. Plus, there was a big incentive; Susan - the snotty bitch - just requested a horse.

"Right' O, Bernie," I replied.

I knew Susan was behind me, so I made a quick about-turn and asked her, mockingly, "Are you a novice rider?"

The nasty demeanor she had in the dining room changed, and was more friendly this time. "Yes," she replied with a soft voice.

'OK. I'll be right back."

I went inside the stables and came out with a comfortable horse.

"Susan, meet Bell. She's calm and easy-going. You and she will get along just fine."

I mounted my horse and shouted to the group of 12 riders, "All novice riders follow me."

Included in my group were Susan and her friends Jackie and Roberta. I was the lead rider but kept Susan close behind me and the others after her.

I turned around and said to Susan, "Where are your other friends? Don't they ride?"

"Oh, they just want to relax and stay by the pool."

When we had girls with bodacious boobs on our rides, for laughs, Bernie, Mike, and I would make their horses trot, so we could watch as their tits bounced up and down, back, and forth. Susan had a sizable pair of jugs and a perfect target for our little prank.

"You know the shirt you're wearing is not the best for riding?" I said to Susan.

"Why, what's wrong with my shirt?"

"You'll find out."

It was a perfect morning - sunny and warm - to go horseback riding. For my novice riders, I chose an easy trail. We crossed a few streams, traversed a grand open field, did a little galloping, but with Susan in mind; it was mostly trotting.

We made a short stop on the trail, and I explained the difference between Western and English riding and gave a quick lesson on how to hold the reigns properly.

When we returned to the stables, everyone's legs, shirt, and hair were mud-splattered. It was a visible sign of a well-executed ride at Arrowhead. The two guys in the group complained they were a little sore. I didn't mind and shouted,

"Hey, wait till tonight; you're gonna need a cold compress on your ass."

"Thanks for getting me a comfortable horse, Steve," Susan said as we dismounted.

"Oh, you're welcome," I replied.

"You liked watching my tits bounce up and down?" Susan said with a smirk.

I just smiled and felt vindicated for her snide remark at breakfast.

Mike and Bernie had me help them for two more rides, but my thoughts were still on Justine. She made none of the morning rides, and I was disappointed not seeing her. What happened? Where was she? After lunch, I went to her room and knocked on the door.

"Justine, it's Steve."

There was no answer. I knocked again, "Justine, it's Steve."

Again, no reply. I heard movement. There was someone in the room.

Wow, she doesn't want to see me! I liked Justine and wanted to get to know her. What went wrong? I knocked again. There was no response, and my heart sank a little. Then, my disappointment and frustration turned to anger.

"Better forget this one, Steve. Heck, there's a crapload of other girls," I said aloud and walked away, pissed.

Saturday night, I got to the lounge a little early and noticed Susan and her girlfriends hanging out at the bar. Before going on stage to play, I strolled over to chat.

All were wearing makeup and western-style clothing. It was a pleasing change in dress and attitude, especially for Susan.

"Good evening, ladies."

Susan was the first to respond.

"Hi, Steve."

"You and your friends must be sore from the ride?" I said.

"Are you kidding? Yes. My back, shoulders, and legs are aching," Susan answered.

Jackie and Roberta nodded their heads in agreement.

"I have a remedy for everyone's aches."

"What's that?" Roberta asked.

"Take two aspirins. That'll help ease the soreness."

I looked at the clock.

"Hey, it's 10 PM, time to get back on the stage. Will I see you later, Susan?" I asked.

"Yeah, I'll be here."

That night, the lounge had loads of thirsty customers, and the dance floor was teeming with people. There wasn't an inch of open space anywhere. It was also sweltering in the heat of the evening. Despite the fresh mountain air flowing through open doors and windows, the lounge percolated in a soupy mixture of cigarette smoke and a potent smell of beer, booze, and body sweat.

The Zigg Zaggs put on a good show. We played songs from the Rolling Stones, Animals, Paul Butterfield Blues

Band, and the Young Bloods. All the while we played, I thought about Justine and looked for her in the crowd. She wasn't at the bar, the dance floor, nowhere. But dancing up in front of the group was Susan.

A nerdy looking guy was hitting on her. I wanted Susan for myself, but all I could do was watch. She danced with him, but Susan often looked up at me, as if to say, "Help."

Mr. Nerdy continued his pursuit. Finally, Susan whispered something in his ear, and he quickly walked off.

When we finished our last set at 2 AM, Susan hung out at the bar, alone without her friends.

I came over to her and asked, "Hi, where's your boyfriend?"

"That nerd?"

"Yeah."

"He's gone."

"What did you whisper in his ear?"

"I told him I have a vaginal infection."

"You do?"

"No, you dope. That's what I say to all the men when I don't want them near me."

"Let's go somewhere, Steve."

"Go somewhere? Where?"

"Your room."

Susan's turnaround attitude was surprising, but I could not pass up such an invitation. Again, I was faced with my recurring problem.

"We can't. The guys in the band are there. What about your room?"

"My girlfriends are there."

"Let's walk over to the pool," I said.

As we walked towards it, Susan softly said, "I like you, Mr. Cowboy."

"I like you too, Susan."

The pool was not the best place for romance, but it was quiet, and nobody was around. We had sex on the most comfortable spot, the lounge chair.

The next morning, I awoke to incredible itching and scratching. My skin was on fire from the cluster of mosquito bites all over my ass and legs. After getting dressed, I went to the office to see Paula, the office secretary. I knew she could help.

"Paula, where's the calamine lotion? I know Whitey has it hidden somewhere."

"Got bug bites?"

"Yes."

Paula searched for a few moments.

"Here it is, Stevie."

"Thanks, Paula."

I raced downstairs to the privacy of the lounge bathroom and soaked myself.

At lunchtime, I entered the dining room and saw Susan at a table with her friends - she too was scratching. All the girls had grins on their faces when they saw me. They knew what happened.

I smiled at everyone, took a seat, but kept quiet and ordered my lunch.

When Jackie, Roberta, Ann, and Margie left the table to go riding, I asked, "Want some calamine lotion, Susan?"

"Yes."

"Follow me."

"Paula," I asked, standing with Susan, "can I have a little more calamine, please?"

Paula was discreet. She looked at Susan, then me, and understood what was going on. She smiled, gave me the bottle, and I handed it to Susan.

"I'll be right back with this," Susan said as she grabbed the lotion from my hand.

She went to her room with the bottle and returned 10 minutes later.

"Thank you, Paula," she said, putting the lotion on the office counter.

It was Tuesday morning, the final day of the holiday weekend. I was exhausted from the little sleep and partying each night till dawn. One thing was still gnawing at my mind, Justine. I couldn't understand what went wrong?

As I entered the lobby to get breakfast, to my amazement, I encountered Susan and Justine chatting. I did an instant 180 about-turn and speed-walked back to my room.

The guys in the band left for Brooklyn early, so my room was empty. I paced back and forth and wondered what was going on? Did Susan and Justine know each other?

Are they exchanging stories about me? How do I manage this one?

There was a knock on my door.

"Steve, it's Justine."

I froze.

Justine? She probably spoke with Susan. Oh, I'm dead meat.

"Steve, can I come in?"

"Yes. It's open."

I felt uneasy when Justine walked inside but was glad to see her.

"What happened to you? I knocked on your door several times, and you didn't answer. You weren't interested in me?" I asked.

"Steve, I was so sick and didn't want to see anyone. That's why I didn't come to the door when you knocked."

"Sick?"

"Too many scotch and sodas."

"Are you OK now?"

"Yeah. Well, I came to say goodbye."

"Goodbye? Where are you going?"

"Home to Brooklyn."

She looked at me, paused, and waited for a reply.

I thought Justine had rejected me, and in my impulsiveness and anger, turned to Susan for satisfaction. Now I felt stupid and guilty.

Justine was soft-spoken, amiable, eager to please, and exceptionally beautiful. She had a genuine sincerity about her, and by her eyes and body posture, I could tell she wanted a positive response from me.

"Are you leaving now?" I asked.

"Yes, Carol and I are heading home."

"Hey, I have the day off tomorrow. Could you give me a ride back to Brooklyn?"

"Yeah, of course."

I met Justine and Carol in the parking lot. They were leaning on a pristine white 1967 Mustang.

"Nice car," I said enthusiastically.

Justine dangled the keys.

"Wanna drive it?" She said with a taunting smile.

I took the keys, and we all got in.

It was a three-hour drive back to Brooklyn. Carol sat in the back seat - did most of the talking - and Justine, in front, most of the listening. We arrived at my apartment building in Brooklyn around 9 PM. I got out and kissed Justine.

"Can I have your phone number?" I asked.

Justine wrote it on a torn piece of paper and gave it to me.

"I'll call you tomorrow. Good night, drive safe."

Justine and I saw each other, off and on, for several years. We had an excellent rapport, always had fun, and enjoyed each other's company. She hinted about getting married on several occasions, but I wasn't ready to commit. I heard she became engaged in 1978. When I reminisce about Arrowhead, it includes thoughts of Justine.

Cavalcade of Characters

Arrowhead attracted a fascinating group. The riding and ski instructors, the kitchen crew, even its guests, everyone had unusual habits and a unique personal story. There was a constant flow of fresh faces that made the interactions between staff and guests intriguing. Some loved it so much they came weekend after weekend, others, only once.

Dishwashers

One position at Arrowhead with the highest turnover was the dishwasher. No one wanted the lowly, unglamorous, hot, and messy job. The only people to fill the spot were social rejects, ex-cons, or drunks. Oh, boy, could they drink.

Old Joe was probably not that old, but his alcohol addiction dried his skin like a prune, aging him 25 years. Joe was a hardworking man and in the kitchen early each day, promptly at 7:00 AM. He was friendly and likable while sober. But his sobriety would last only three weeks. At the end of that time, he would binge drink. The entire staff knew when Joe was off the wagon; Whitey would be in the kitchen screaming and cursing when Joe didn't show up for work.

When I came into the kitchen to have breakfast one morning, pots, pans, plates, and cooking utensils were piled high, still waiting for the dishwashing machine.

Whitey stomped his feet as he paced back and forth.

"God Damn that old bastard," Whitey yelled.

"What's wrong, Whitey?" I asked.

"That old shit head is drunk again and locked in his room."

"What shit head?"

"Stefano, come with me."

We walked briskly to Joe's staff-house room and stood by the door.

"Joe, are you in there?" Whitey yelled as he pounded on the door. There wasn't any answer.

"Joe. Wake up," Whitey shouted and punched the door.

Whitey lost his temper and kicked the door open with his foot. My jaw dropped. In his underwear, Joe was passed out on the floor, in a fetal position with each arm wrapped around a half-finished 5th of Johnny Walker.

Surrounding him was a sea of empty whiskey bottles, wall to wall. We couldn't enter Joe's room without stepping on a bottle. How could a man drink that much alcohol and live?

"Stefano, grab his feet."

I grabbed Joe by the ankles; Whitey grabbed his arms.

"Where are we taking him?" I asked.

"We're gonna take this old shit bastard and throw him in the lake!"

Still unconscious from his drunken stupor, we held Joe by his extremities and marched him outside and down to the lake. When Whitey and I got to the edge of the water, we hurled the old geezer in it.

Joe hit the shallow part of the lake on all fours and abruptly woke up.

"Joe, are you alive?" Whitey asked.

"Yeah, I'll be OK once I get back to my room."

Whitey put his hands-on-hips and shouted, "Joe, now that you're sober, get dressed and get your fuck'n ass in the kitchen and start washing dishes."

Big E - another dishwasher - was an all-purpose do-little. Nobody knew why he called himself that name, but he was fat - shaped like a giant pear - shy and had verbal diarrhea. He couldn't stop talking. Whenever you asked Big E a question, he would answer by adding an excess of irrelevant facts making it an agonizingly long answer. His favorite pastime was eating and disappearing when he was needed.

Once, I foolishly asked, "Hey Big E, what's for lunch?"

"I think we're have'n steak, but maybe it's chicken. You like chicken Steve'O? I like chicken too. I'd rather have hamburgers than chicken. Chicken isn't good unless you fry it in oil. I like deep-fried chicken but without the skin. The skin gives me gas. I hate gas cause I get the shits right after," he replied.

I couldn't take his nonstop talking and quickly slipped away. Big E continued his rant - despite me being 100 ft. from him - and kept shouting, "I think we're also have'n mashed potatoes, I love mashed potatoes and gravy, Steve'O."

None of the staff could tolerate or talk with Big E for longer than a few minutes.

There were other dishwashers: Milton Deluxe from the Equator of the Moon, Handsome Harry, and Buffalo Bob. The job had a conveyer belt of screwballs and drunks with peculiar names and personal stories. If they worked at Arrowhead for longer than three weeks, it was a miracle.

Arrowhead Cooks

The second-highest turnover in jobs was the cook. Whitey was a competent chef and did it for the small number of guests and staff during the week but hated it. He preferred fixing a junk car or bailing hay for the horses rather than being stuck in the hot greasy kitchen cooking for 200 or even 10 people. When someone, anyone, applied for the spot as the cook, Whitey was happy to hire them.

Harvey and his wife came to Arrowhead as guests one weekend. He was a short, grumpy bearded man who wore western-style clothes and had a wooden leg. His wife, a slovenly behemoth weighing 300 lbs, was a quiet person who dressed poorly and hardly said a word. Together, they were a pair sent directly from Hollywood's Central Casting.

While eating dinner, Harvey bragged to everyone about his culinary talents. Whitey seized the opportunity and offered him the job to cook at Arrowhead, no questions asked. The only stipulation was Harvey's wife. She would have to be Harvey's assistant and waitress.

I often had breakfast at a small table in the kitchen. From that spot, I could view Arrowhead Lake and enjoy the warm summer breezes blowing in from the screen door.

One Sunday morning, as I ate, Harvey proudly exclaimed, "Hey Stevie, watch this."

I looked up to see Harvey juggling two 10-inch kitchen knives in the air, which landed, point first, on the front side of his wooden leg. He repeated his circus act several times.

"I didn't know you could juggle, Harvey?"

"Yes, I can, Stevie. I'm a man of many talents."

"Doesn't that put big holes in your leg?" I asked.

"Yeah, but I have three more legs in my room. Do you want to see me juggle pots and pans?"

"No, Harvey. I've got to get to work. Maybe some other time?"

Rocco was a big swarthy young Italian man of 250 lbs and had an upbeat, kind nature. As a guest one weekend, he was unimpressed with Whitey's bland, tasteless cuisine. He put his fork down and boldly said, "Whitey, this food sucks.

I can do a better job with my eyes closed."

"OK, Rocco, you can cook for me anytime," Whitey happily replied.

Rocco went into the kitchen, threw two whole chickens in a pot, mixed herbs, spices, and whatever ingredients he could find available, and whipped up a delicious batch of chicken cacciatore. Everyone devoured it, and Whitey hired him.

Not only was he an excellent cook, but Rocco also loved to sing. He was not Pavarotti, but he had a natural voice and enjoyed expressing it. When Rocco prepared his meals, he would sing many of the Doo-Wop songs from the 1950s.

His favorite was the hit by Dean Martin, "That's Amore." Rocco would sing, *When the moon hits your eye like a big pizza pie, that's amore.* then laugh and say, "I should be a recording artist than slinging hash at this dump."

On Saturday nights, when the Zigg Zaggs were performing, we would often invite Rocco to join us for his rendition of *"That's Amore."* The crowd would stop their chatter and listen to him flex his melodic vocal cords.

Wild Bill - a certified oddball - also had the job as Arrowhead's culinary master, but for only a short time. Bill had the peculiar grin of Alice in Wonderland's Cheshire cat. He seemed an affable fellow, but I didn't trust him. We awoke one day to find him missing. Bill was nowhere to be found, and neither was $5000, which he stole from the Arrowhead safe.

Riding Instructors

Was it their good looks, macho physique, blatant uncouth behavior, or the odiferous bouquet of horses that attracted the ladies? It's hard to say, but the riding instructors were the top celebrities at Arrowhead and the key draw for the single girls.

Weekend guests would leave their Manhattan jobs on Friday, after work, and drive on Route 17 upstate to Arrowhead. Many would not arrive until 10, or as late as 11 PM. Once they signed in at the front desk, the ladies and gents would quickly unpack, refresh themselves from the long drive and slowly stroll to the lounge.

As they waited for the ladies to appear, the riding instructors positioned themselves strategically at the bar to view the parade of single girls marching towards them. The lengthy walk - about 75 feet - offered ample time to size-up the bevy of beauties.

To enhance their sexual attraction, the riding instructors often dressed in western attire - cowboy boots and hats, large silver-buckled belts, jeans, and western-style shirts. Some even developed a slight southern accent, despite coming from Brooklyn and the Bronx.

As the ladies approached, the comments from the riding instructors would overflow.

"Look at the shape of this one."

"Ooh, too much makeup."

"Wow, what a set of jugs."

The female guests sitting at the bar also made quiet remarks about the men. Their comments were just as harsh and crude.

"What jail did they let this one out of?"

"Does he have permission from his mother?"

By 11 PM, most guests got acquainted via small talk or dancing to the music. On any summer weekend, the lounge would be packed with 150 - 250 people. It was easy for a guy to meet a girl. Even if you were a pimple-faced loser, you could, at the very least, get a phone number. The gals did just as well as the guys.

It was a meat market, not a place for thin-skinned temperaments or the meek. Arrowhead attracted a hard-working middle-class crowd who wanted to unwind and ride horses - until they had sores on their asses - eat and party all night.

Unique ways

The riding instructors had an advantage over the regular male guests and were the most popular with the ladies. Some of the staff that didn't work in the stables had other unique ways of attracting women.

Pete was a handsome, 6ft tall, mustachioed young man from Queens, New York. He played guitar, owned a horse, and was a carefree likable guy. Whitey noticed his troubadour-like abilities and hired him to sing Country and Western songs so the guests could appreciate the flavor of the west. His singing minstrel show made him popular with everyone at Arrowhead and the single girls.

Pete had no trouble attracting the best-looking gals. He was articulate and liked to chat. Yet, with those admirable assets, Pete had a penchant for the homeliest, oddest, and weird-looking girls rather than seeking the attractive ones.

I sat with him at the bar one evening, and curiously asked, "Pete, why do you prefer the odd-looking weirdo gals over the hot attractive ones?"

"Well, Stevie," he smiled, "I like them that way for many reasons. One, they never refuse me. Two, I don't have to work hard. Three, they pay for their drinks. And four, I'm doing a good deed."

I laughed, "Oh, now I understand. So, Pete, we can say you're performing a service for all those less fortunate ladies?"

"Yeah, I guess you could say that, Stevie."

Whenever a strange-looking gal walked into the bar, I took comfort in knowing that Pete was ready to go where no man had gone before.

Jared, too, was tall, good-looking, and fair-haired, but had the opposite approach from Pete's. While Pete would work his magic quietly at a corner spot, Jared would be the loudest, most obnoxious, testy person at the bar. His boisterous ways made him a great party guy that added flavor to the mix at Arrowhead. One would think that his aggressive, sometimes offensive attitude would turn the girls off. But no. It turned them on.

Despite Jared's egocentricities and hyperbole about his female conquests, he was always with a girl and never without. He bragged one time - when many of the male staffers were hanging out a the bar - that at 25, he already had sex with over 300 girls. All the guys burst into laughter. Not one of us believed his incredible story. But in retrospect, I think he was telling the truth. And then there was Jule.

He was an easygoing man of 24 years. He arrived as a guest on Memorial Day and boasted about his swimming skills. Whitey, in need of a lifeguard for the pool, overheard his brag and gave him free weekends in exchange for his services.

We liked Jule. His good humor and cheerful attitude made him popular with the guests. He joined the ranks of the Arrowhead celebrities with a unique pick-up line, the best I ever heard.

While sitting at the bar chatting with a female guest, he removed his cowboy hat, and with a straight face, he said, "Excuse me, mam, but I'd like to thank your mother and father."

"Oh, why is that?" she replied.

"For making such a beautiful person as you."

It was super corny, but it worked every time.

Goodbye Zigg Zaggs

The Zigg Zaggs performed at Arrowhead throughout the winter of 1969. In the spring of 1970, a significant change occurred, the draft.

The Vietnam War was raging and required more young men to fight. The US government instituted a lottery number system to enlarge the pool of draftees. While televised, a congressman randomly selected a number from a large glass jar, which coincided with someone's birthdate. If the number chosen corresponded to your birthday, you were going to Vietnam.

The only exceptions permitted were a college deferment or a rating of 4F - given to men with severe physical disabilities. Arty, our drummer, freaked when his number was called. He wasn't in college, didn't have a handicap, and had no intention of going to Vietnam. Shortly after, he fled to Canada to avoid the draft.

When he told me of his decision to leave the band, my heart sank, but I was more saddened to lose a long-time friend. We kept in touch by mail and telephone, but we didn't see each other ever again.

Arty was a significant figure in the Zigg Zaggs. Once he was gone, I knew it would be the end of the band. Alan and Anthony, the other members, were exempt from the draft because of their asthma. I hoped they would weather the rough times, but they also felt the itch to leave and went their separate ways. I was still in college and entitled to my student deferment.

No matter what I did or said, there was no preventing the Zigg Zagg's demise. My hope of becoming a rock star faded with the breakup.

I tried to reorganize the band with other musicians but found the mix of new guys conflicting. It was discouraging and unsettling.

Arrowhead Part 2

Traveling Troubadours

Pete - Arrowhead's singing minstrel - was temporarily living in Queens, New York, with his parents. He called me in the early summer of 1970 with an exciting offer.

"Hey, Stevie, I teamed up with a bass player. We've got a gig at a Country and Western bar and grill in Valhalla, New York. Are you interested in playing lead guitar?"

Singing Country and Western music wasn't my thing, but nobody else was banging down my door. Pete's offer uplifted my spirits.

"Sounds good to me, Pete. When do we start?"

"In two weeks, but I'll speak with you before that."

"Thanks for thinking of me, Pete."

"Don't mention it, Stevie."

Two weeks later, I drove to Pete's home on Utopia Parkway, Queens. He was outside, waiting for me.

"Hi, Stevie. Ready to go?"

"Yep. Let me get my guitar and amp."

Pete and I loaded our gear into his 57 Chevy and drove up the Taconic State Parkway to Valhalla, New York. We were in a cheerful mood and happy to be busy.

"Stevie, after we work at *Little Texas*, I lined up a few other joints for us to play."

What's *Little Texas* like, Pete? Is it a dump? Are there any single girls hanging out there?"

"It's a nice place, not too bad, Stevie. I think you'll like it. But for girls, I have no idea."

We pulled up to the *Little Texas Bar and Grill* and parked in the lot. Waiting for us outside was Pete's friend, Barney, a tall skinny guy with a protruding Adam's apple. He was a character right out of Mad Magazine.

"Steve, this is my friend Barney."

"Hi, Barney, glad to meet you."

"Pleased to meet ya, Steve."

We grabbed our stuff and went inside. When we entered, Country and Western music played on the Juke Box, and interesting Texas and Western memorabilia covered the walls. It seemed like an authentic piece of the old west in New York. But there was one big problem. Save for the two people drinking at the bar, no one else was there, and it quickly brought back memories of the Zigg Zagg's first night at Arrowhead.

"Pete. Does it get busy here?" I asked.

"Yeah, it looks bad, but give it time. It'll pick up."

"Where do we set up?"

"Right there, Stevie."

I turned to look at where Pete was pointing. It was a tiny wooden stage and had barely enough room for the three of us, our guitars, Barney's upright bass, and my Fender amp and microphone. By the time we were ready to do the night's first song, *Little Texas* had a full crowd.

All worked out well that night. We thought it was a good idea to dress in western-style clothes for our repeat gigs at *Little Texas*. I wore my 2.5 inches wide, handmade western belt with a large silver buckle, jeans, and cowboy boots. Pete and Barney wore less traditional western clothes: jeans, sneakers, and plain western-style white shirts.

Porter Corners

"Where's our next gig, Pete?" I asked while driving home from our final time at *Little Texas*.

"It's a lounge outside of Albany, Stevie."

"That's a long drive from Queens."

"Yes, it is, but I have a good idea."

"What's that?"

"We rest one day when we get back home, then you meet me in Queens, and we'll drive to the house I just bought in Porter Corners."

"Porter Corners? Where's Porter Corners?"

"Not too far from Saratoga and the racetrack."

"Oh, it's a house in the country."

"Yup. We stay there a couple of days and travel to the Dude Ranches and lounges that are close by."

"OK. I'm in."

Two days later, Pete and I loaded his 57 Chevy with our guitars, my Fender amp, and Prince - his white German Shepherd - and drove to his country home in the sticks.

After a 3-hour drive, we turned on to a long dirt road that led to the front door of Pete's place. It was an old house - circa 1930s - and way off the grid. Everything in it was outdated, the kitchen, bathroom, furniture, electric wiring, and the plumbing. The big attraction was the 90 acres of beautiful maple trees and its isolation. For Pete, it was just right.

We brought our stuff into the kitchen as Prince wagged his tail, escorting us inside. Pete pointed to my room, which was next to the kitchen.

"Stevie, this is yours."

I plopped my duffle bag on the floor and looked around. It was a small bedroom with a distinct musty odor of not being used and reminded me of Arrowhead's attic. When I sat on the one-person bed to test it out, a small cloud of dust puffed up around me. Coughing, I quickly opened its only window.

"Humm, I thought. Home for the next few days."

"Stevie. Want a beer?" Pete called out from the kitchen.

"Yeah, Pete. What about something to eat?"

"Well, there's a small problem."

"What's that?" I asked, walking into the kitchen.

"I only have dog biscuits," Pete replied, laughing.

"Dog biscuits? That's all? How do they taste with a beer, Pete?"

"Not too bad. They're a little crunchy, but the beer softens them a bit."

"Stevie," Pete said as we dined on our biscuits and drank our beers, "I only have 10 bucks in my pocket. So, I found some work for us at the Saratoga racetrack."

"What kind of work, Pete?"

"Fixing a metal roof on one of the stables. It'll keep us busy for the next 5 days until our gig at the *Longhorn Lounge.*

"What'll they pay us?"

"Good money. $25 a day, each."

"When do we start?"

"Tomorrow."

After our beer and biscuits, Pete gave me a walking tour of his property.

"Once I get enough money, Stevie, I'm going to thin out these maple trees and make a few improvements in the kitchen."

"Sounds good, Pete. What time do we start work tomorrow?"

"Early. Let's head back and get some rest."

I was hungry and reluctantly grabbed 3 dog biscuits and a beer from the fridge. Pete didn't have a TV, so there wasn't anything else to do but get into bed. Price followed me into my room, and curiously laid down beside me.

"Stevie, is Prince with you?" Pete called out from his bedroom.

'Yes. Is that OK?"

"Yeah. You should be honored," Pete replied.

"Why?" I asked.

"He doesn't like anybody. You must have that special smell."

I looked at Prince and petted him on the head.

"Good boy, Prince. Good boy."

We awoke early the next morning and drove to the Saratoga racetrack. A few workmen were already there working on the metal roof when we arrived. Pete walked over to the foreman, spoke with him, then came back.

"Here's the deal, Stevie. You and me will assist the regular guys in leveling the roof. Whatever materials and supplies they need, we'll get it for them. Everyone breaks for lunch at noon and goes home at 4 PM."

"OK, Pete. Whatever you say."

We spent 4 days securing and strengthening the metal roof that sat over the stable. The work was hard and sweaty but worth the effort. Pete and I earned $100 each. After getting paid, we celebrated by buying real food at the supermarket and stuffed ourselves at the local diner. Prince also got a present, a greasy steak dinner.

Pete was a great manager. He arranged other small western-style bars and a few Dude Ranches in upper New York State to sing and earn money. More importantly, it was great for me to be playing music.

I was still in college, and the summer of 1970 was approaching. Playing the Country and Western circuit on the weekends with Pete and Barney wasn't enough work to occupy my summer break. I had an idea and called Pete.

"Hi, Pete. How are you?"

"Good, Stevie. How are you? What's going on?"

"Pete, I have an idea and thought I'd run it by you."

"Yeah, what's that, Stevie?"

"What do you think about bringing our Country and Western act to Arrowhead?"

"Well, I never thought about it, but it sounds like a good idea."

"What about Barney? Do you think he would come with us?" I asked

"I spoke with him yesterday. He's having problems with his wife, so I think he's out," Pete replied.

"Oh, that's too bad. I liked Barney."

"Pete, I'm going to call Whitey and see what he says."

"OK, Stevie, get back to me."

I hung up and called the Ranch.

"Hello, Arrowhead," Whitey answered.

"Hi, Whitey. It's Steve. How are you?"

"Oh, pretty good."

"Pete and I want to come to Arrowhead and play guitar on the weekend to entertain the guests. What do you think?"

"Er, well, I can't pay you guys very much. Maybe $50 each and give you the weekend free."

"That's sounds good to me. Let me tell Pete, and I'll call you back."

"OK."

"Pete, he agreed to our idea."

"How much money will he pay us, Stevie?"

"50 bucks each plus free room and board."

Each weekend that summer, Pete and I drove from Queens to Arrowhead. On Saturday afternoons, and at the 5 PM cocktail hour in the lounge, we'd sing our duets. With our minstrel act, I could listen to the band that replaced the Zigg Zaggs and ride the horses. The money sucked, but I didn't care. It was something to do in the summer, and best of all, Arrowhead was always loaded with girls.

Whitey was in the lounge one Sunday afternoon, and I came over to collect our $100. He was behind the bar with a long sour face.

"Whitey, Pete, and I are heading home. Can I get our $100? Hey, you don't look so good. What's wrong?"

Whitey slowly reached into his pocket, gave me the $100, then blurted out in anger, "That cozucker bastard cook just quit on me. Hey, Stefano, you wanna job as a cook?"

When Rocco needed a hand in the kitchen, I would help with food preparation and small jobs. He taught me how to make eggs, pancakes, and French toast, things a short-order cook would make. It was fun. Whitey had quietly noticed my little-known talent but said nothing until now, his moment of despair.

"Me, cook? Who told you I could cook?"

"I watched ya help Rocco. The staff sez yer cook'n was better than his."

Whitey could be strange. If I pissed him off, he might not let me play guitar at Arrowhead. How could I attract the girls if I was the greasy-fingered cook?

"What'd you have in mind, Whitey?"

The following week my duffle bag was packed for the summer, and again, I was on my way up Route 17 West to Arrowhead. This time was different. I had a car, was earning $100 per week, cooking only Monday to Friday, and the weekends free. Now that was a deal.

Egg Yolks for Eyes

The weekdays were slow and easy-going, which gave me ample time to settle in and adjust to my newly acquired status. No longer was I an Arrowhead riding instructor, maintenance man, or player in the band. I was the cook.

Whitey and I discussed what to serve during the week. He suggested planning the daily lunch and dinner meals, and then I would repeat the same combination throughout the summer. It was a great idea.

Breakfast was simple. Guests could have eggs - any type - a choice of French toast or pancakes and bacon. We had either meatloaf, Salisbury steak, chicken cacciatore, spaghetti and meatballs, or chopped steak and onions, simple good things for lunch or dinner. It was a modest system that worked.

On the upcoming July 4th weekend, Whitey booked 325 guests, way more than the small staff could handle. He approached me on Thursday before the holiday.

"Hey Stefano, er, well, can you work this weekend, er, uh, I won't be able to do all the cooking alone?" he asked.

If I said no, someone would have to pick up the slack doing the extra work in the kitchen. Plus, Whitey didn't care if the staff had trouble managing the overload of guests. I paused and let him hang for a minute.

"Yeah, OK," I said reluctantly.

Friday afternoon, before the big weekend, I was anxious. Scrambled eggs and bacon were the most popular breakfast. To make it for a few people was easy. Multiply that by 325; it was a killer.

How was I going to manage all those egg orders? I'd be swamped and never make it out of the kitchen alive. Later that day, I conceived a terrific idea, a unique egg concoction for the holiday breakfast onslaught.

In the kitchen Friday night, I assessed what food supplies we had. There was plenty on hand, especially eggs. I took 4 grosses of eggs from the walk-in fridge, cracked each one open, poured and mixed their contents in an enormous stainless-steel pot, and added a quart of milk.

I grabbed a soup ladle and dipped it into my goopy yellow blend. Each full scoop measured two eggs. When an order of scrambled eggs would come in, I'd grab the ladle and cut the time spent cracking open each egg.

To test if my concoction worked, I poured it onto the grill, cooked, and ate it.

"Umm, it's good."

Saturday morning, I awoke extra early and was the first to arrive in the kitchen at 6 AM. I lit the big 3ft. X 2ft. cast iron grill, made pounds of fresh bacon and removed my mixture from the walk-in fridge.

"Good morning, Sandy, Roberta, Irene," I said, greeting my weekend waitresses as they came into the kitchen.

Roberta quickly ran to the dining hall doors. Before unlocking them, she peered through its windows and could see the hungry guests were pacing in the lobby.

"Steve, they're here," Roberta signaled back.

"OK, girls, are we ready?"

They nodded, "Yes."

Roberta opened the flood gates. The mob quickly burst in and rapidly filled every seat. Sandy, Roberta, and Irene rolled up their sleeves and took their orders.

Roberta came blasting through the kitchen doors, yelling, "6 scrambled eggs, 2 light, 2 dry, 2 soft."

"2 scrambled dry, 2 French toast," Sandy said, standing behind Roberta.

"2 eggs over, 2 French toast, 1 pancake," Irene yelled.

All three waitresses repeated orders like that at a furious pace.

Like a machine, I was hurling the soup ladle - from the pot to the grill - scrambling, pouring pancakes, making French toast, and flipping bacon in a ferocious assault. My blend was working.

Sandy, Roberta, and Irene flew in and out of the kitchen - their hands holding either breakfast orders or empty dishes - and the double-hinged kitchen doors made a loud, whooshing sound as the three of them passed through it.

After an hour of the hectic pace, I became crazed. Each time the girls raced back into the kitchen, I saw egg yolks in place of their eyes. It was intense. All was going well, but for one obnoxious guest.

Sandy came over to me and whispered in my ear.

"Steve, there's a guest that doesn't like the eggs you made him."

"What's wrong with the eggs?"

"He wants them wet, not dry."

"OK. I'll make his eggs the way he likes."

I dipped my ladle into the pot and gently scrambled the eggs, wet, not dry.

"Sandy, wet eggs for Mr. Picky," I yelled.

Sandy took the order and went back to the dining hall. She was gone for about three minutes and returned with his untouched plate of eggs. I looked at her and she at me.

"What's wrong now?" I asked.

"He says the eggs are too wet."

"Oh, that fuck'n hump."

While Sandy waited, I scrambled two more eggs, not too wet, not too dry.

"Sandy, here's Mr. Fuck Face's order. Now they're perfect."

Sandy grabbed the plate and walked back into the dining hall. She returned a minute later with the plate of eggs. I looked at Sandy and cursed, "Oh, that piece of shit! What now?"

"He'd like them a bit dryer."

"OK. Now he's gonna get my special recipe."

I dipped the ladle into the pot and poured the eggs onto the grill. While stirring the mixture with my fork, I gathered a glob of saliva and spat into the eggs. Sandy's eyes rolled, and then she burst into laughter. Everyone in the kitchen also laughed.

"Take this to Mr. Asshole. He should like it this time."

Sandy grabbed the plate, pushed open the double-hinged kitchen doors, and walked back into the dining hall.

She returned, empty-handed, a few moments later. There was silence in the kitchen.

"Well?" I asked.

Sandy laughed and replied, "Mr. Asshole loved them. He said, "Now, that's the way I like it.""

You Cun Go!

After the tumult of July 4th weekend, life at Arrowhead settled down for the rest of the summer. There were no complaints about breakfast, and everyone enjoyed my simple cooking.

It couldn't have been better for me. There was money in my pocket, the weekends were free from work, and I had a car to travel anywhere.

I initially thought being stuck in the hot, steamy kitchen flipping burgers, smelling like bacon, and scrambling eggs would make it difficult, perhaps impossible, to attract girls. Strangely, it had the opposite effect. It turned them on.

Several girls from Manhattan were on vacation and spending the first week of August at the Ranch. Trying to be friendly, I came out from the kitchen and served them their breakfast on the second day of their weeklong stay.

"Hi, I'm Steve. Who gets the pancakes?"

"Me," said one of them.

"Scrambled eggs?"

"That's me," said another.

I turned to the last one, "So, the French toast is yours?"

"Yes," she answered.

"Welcome to Arrowhead. What're your names?" I asked.

"I'm Linda."

"Stacy."

"Beth."

Linda, the most outspoken, asked condescendingly, "Are you our waiter?"

"No. I'm the cook," I replied and went back to the kitchen.

At 11 AM, I prepared the lunchtime meal when Sandy – the Arrowhead waitress - brought Linda, Stacy, and Beth in the kitchen.

"Steve, the girls were curious to see how you cooked the meals. Can they watch?" Sandy asked.

It was an unusual request, but it was a slow and uneventful week.

"Yeah."

"What are you making us for lunch, Steve?" Linda asked.

First, she plays the bitch, and now it's time to be nice? This one is interested in more than cooking. I'll play along with her.

"Hi, Linda. We're having meatloaf," I replied.

"Do you want some help, Steve?" Linda asked.

I didn't want help but was curious to know why she was acting nice?

"Yeah, you can help me."

I turned to her two friends Beth and Stacy, "What about you guys?"

"Oh, we're going to watch," Stacy answered.

"OK. Stand back a bit and give Linda and me some room."

I gave Linda a large wooden spoon.

"With this," I said, "stir and fold the meat, add salt, a little parsley, eggs, and breadcrumbs while I get a pan to put it in."

I came back with the pan and placed it next to Linda.

"How are you doing, Linda?" I asked.

"I love playing with the meat, Steve," she replied, smiling.

My eyebrows went up, and so did Stacy's and Beth's.

"OK, Ladies. It's time to put the meatloaf in the oven. Come back at 1 PM for lunch. It'll be ready, then."

At lunchtime, Sandy served the guests and came back through the double-hinged kitchen doors laughing.

"What's so funny, Sandy?' I asked.

"Your girlfriend was praising your meatloaf."

"My girlfriend? Are you referring to Linda?"

"Yes."

"What'd she say?"

"It's delicious. The best she ever had."

Whitey showed a movie in the lounge that evening to entertain the guests and staff. I was sitting at the bar chatting with Bernie when Linda, Beth, and Stacy entered and rambled towards us. I lifted my drink to acknowledge them.

"Good evening, ladies."

"Hi, Steve," Linda said with a friendly smile.

"Hi, Linda. Gonna watch the movie?"

"Yeah, what movie are we watching?"

"The Magnificent Seven."

"What's it about?"

"It's a Western. You like Westerns?"

"I don't know?"

"Well, it's the only entertainment we have tonight."

"Oh, why don't you entertain me?"

With Linda, everything had a double meaning. Not surprised by her provocative statements, I played the dummy.

"What kind of entertainment do you like? Do you want to sing? Dance?" I asked.

She paused, then replied, "No. Let's go to your room."

"Oh? Do you want to see my art collection?"

With a confused expression, she asked, "Art?"

"Ah, yes. I have a wall full of modern art posters."

Not sure if I was telling the truth, Linda's eyebrows went up, and she paused again.

"OK. Let's go."

We walked to the staff house, and I lead Linda up the stairs to the second floor.

"Which one is your room, Steve?" She asked looking at the 4 doors on the second floor.

"None. My room is the attic."

"The attic?" Linda asked.

"Yeah. The coolest place at Arrowhead. It's where I keep my best artwork."

We climb the steps to the attic, and when the door opened, Linda was amazed.

"Wow. You weren't kidding."

Instead of wallpaper, I had the walls covered with posters from advertisements and movies.

"Where did you get these, Steve?"

"I worked at a head shop called People Posters and thought they would make an attractive decoration."

Before I could say another word, Linda wrapped her arms around my back and kissed me aggressively.

"Oh, is this kind of entertainment you had in mind, Linda?"

"Yes, but you have to be careful."

"Careful? What do you mean, careful?"

Linda took off her clothes and got on my bed.

"Yes. You can do anything you want to me but don't touch my hair."

For a moment, I was bewildered and stepped back.

"Your hair?"

"Yes. I have a metal plate in my head, so you have to be careful."

"Ah, OK. I'll keep that in mind."

For the rest of her vacation at Arrowhead, Linda and I had a good time. We shared drinks in the lounge, spent time at the pool, and one evening, we drove to Jack and Jil's.

When she left Arrowhead for home, Linda never said goodbye. She was no different than many of the girls I met there. Once they had their itch satisfied, it was over - no goodbye or exchange of phone numbers before leaving.

It was mid-August. On a Sunday evening, after dinner was over, I strolled into the lounge and noticed Whitey alone behind the bar. He had an open bottle of Johnny Walker in hand. He was drunk and angry.

"What's up, Whitey?"

"Stefano, you fucked me."

"I fucked you? What are you talking about?"

"You dook advanmage of me. I hate cook'n. You was suposta cook on da weekend doo."

Whitey didn't like the deal we struck. Now, in his drunken stupor, his hidden anger towards me surfaced.

"That was the agreement we made. Why did you agree to it if you didn't like it?" I replied.

He pointed to the lounge door, "You cun go, Stefano."

"Now, right now, you want me to leave?"

"Yeah, now."

Oh, that fuckhead. That sneaky shitheaded bastard. It's only two more weeks until the end of the summer. He knows he can get by without me.

There was no use in arguing. It wouldn't make a difference.

"OK, pay me for the week, and I'll go, "I replied with an angry tone.

He reached into his pocket and gave me $200. I grabbed it from his hand and stormed out of the lounge.

My duffle bag was packed Monday morning, and I was ready to make the long trip back home. Before leaving, I walked up to the barn to say goodbye to the guys.

"Steve, we heard the news," Mike said as he was brushing a horse.

"Yeah, Mike. Oh, well, I'll find something else to do for the rest of the summer."

Mike shook my hand, "Steve, You'll be back at college in a few weeks, and you'll be happy."

"I guess so, Mike."

Bernie looked at me with sad eyes and shook my hand. He and Mike tried to ease the disappointment of my sudden departure, but it didn't help.

It was a three-hour trip to Brooklyn. On the ride home, I thought about the remaining weeks of the summer and what to do. My school buddies were still away or had jobs, and there was no one to commiserate with or share the passing time. My biggest fear was being bored. It was repulsive to me and horrible thought. Quickly, my discontent turned to anger.

"I'm not going back to that fuck'n shit hole!"

Strictly Business

It was a year since my unpleasant departure from Arrowhead. I graduated from college and pursued a more practical career as an advertising photographer instead of becoming a rock guitarist.

My life was in limbo. I had no girlfriend, zip to do on the weekend, and the prospects for work as a novice photographer were few. The only place to remedy my stagnating social schedule, where I could mix, mingle, and get back in the groove, was Arrowhead. I hoped to return with no hard feelings between Whitey and myself, but before I did, I'd test the waters.

Early Sunday evening, I called my friend Jerry. He would know all about the good or bad vibes at Arrowhead.

Ring, Ring. "Hello?"

"Jerry, what's shake'n?"

"Not much, Steve. What's going on with you?"

"I was thinking of taking a trip to Arrowhead. What do you think Whitey will say?"

"I don't think he'll say anything, Steve."

"No? He's not still pissed at me?"

"Steve, Whitey forgot about it the moment you were gone."

"No, shit. That's great, Jerry. I was thinking of working as a riding instructor on weekends."

"Call Whitey and see what he has to say."

"OK. I will. Thanks, Jerry."

The following Friday, I was chugging along Route 17 to Arrowhead. Once there, I made a beeline to the lounge and expected to see my old friends, chat with the gang, and party. I was in for a shocking surprise.

The bar and lounge were busy and had that familiar Arrowhead flavor, but it was crowded with unfamiliar faces. The old crew was gone, and I didn't hear the expected, "Hey, Steve, how ya doing" from everyone when I walked inside. Even the band was new. It was awkward and an unsettling feeling.

"Wow, I don't know anyone. I'm a stranger here," I mumbled.

Not being recognized was an odd feeling. But in the alien crowd was a face I knew well, and I walked over to greet him.

"Hey, Whitey, how are yah?"

"Oh, pretty good," he replied in his usual modest fashion.

Sitting next to him was a pretty girl. He introduced us, "Stefano, this is Bernadette," then he quietly walked away.

I sat next to her and introduced myself.

"Hi, I'm Steve. I used to work here."

"Hi Steve, I know all about you."

"You do?"

"Yeah, they told me when they gave me your old attic room. It's the coolest room at Arrowhead."

"Yes. I worked hard, making it cool. When did you start working here, Bernadette?"

"Two months ago."

"I bet you came as a guest."

"Yes, how did you know?"

"That's the way most of the staff get their job."

"What do you do at Arrowhead?"

"I'm a waitress."

"Oh, great."

"Wanna see what I did to your old room, Steve?"

Not wanting to pass up an invitation and great opportunity, I quickly responded, "OK, Bernadette, lead the way."

We left the lounge, walked to the staff house, and up the stairs to the attic. She opened the door, and both of us stepped inside.

I looked around. Most of my decorations were still there, with a few added feminine touches. But my interest wasn't in what she did with the décor.

Bernadette was a lovely, petite gal with an olive-colored complexion and well built. She also had a distinctive, alluring smell of musk oil - a popular perfume at the time. She was a big turn on for me, and I thought I had it *Made in the Shade.*

"I see you kept my posters."

"Yeah, they're nice. I like them."

"There aren't any chairs, Steve," Bernadette said as she pointed to the bed, "you can sit here if you like."

We sat comfortably on the bed. Then, Bernadette moved closer.

Thinking she offered to get more relaxed, I put my arm around her waist.

"So, Bernadette, what do you for fun at Arrowhead?"

"You can call me Bernie if you like."

"OK, Bernie," I replied gladly.

"After me and my boyfriend finish working in the kitchen, we just hang out in the lounge."

Huh? I was confused. Her friendliness and alluring approach were appealing. Then she announced she had a boyfriend?

"Your boyfriend? What boyfriend? I don't see any boyfriend."

"Oh, he isn't here yet. He should be soon."

Abruptly, my big turn-on became a big turn-off, and the thoughts of getting laid vanished. I withdrew my arm from her waist.

Trying to improve my luck while her dufus boyfriend might pop-up from behind the bushes would be stupid. A voice inside my head said, "Steve, time to get back to the lounge and take your chances with someone else."

I stood up from the bed and looked at Bernadette, "Well, nice meeting you. Thanks for showing me my old room."

I bolted from the attic, hurried down the steps, and back to the lounge.

The next day, I spoke with Whitey about working at the Ranch. He had no hard feelings, and we discussed a job as a riding instructor on weekends.

During my year-long hiatus, significant changes occurred that made Arrowhead different. Bernie, Mike, Pete, and most of the former staffers were gone. Arrowhead's new crew was likable, but not as before. The wild-party-anything-goes-pot-smoking atmosphere, which was so attractive, was replaced by a brooding, uptight mood.

A ball-busting nitpicker named Markus was the new foremen of the riding stable. All instructors had one hour to get their riders on the trail, back to the stables, and saddled up for the next gang of waiting guests.

In the kitchen, waitresses could not associate with anyone and be punctual when arriving for work. Even the band took their breaks according to the dictates of the bartender. Now, it was strictly business.

Regardless of these new rules, Arrowhead was still the best place to mix, mingle, enjoy a weekend in upstate New York, and most importantly, meet girls. This time, I kept a low profile, and my mouth shut.

Girls from Bayridge

My career was developing nicely. By 1973, I was the studio manager for a Manhattan advertising photographer. Having a regular paycheck was a confidence builder. I junked my 62 Ford and bought a sporty sexy muscle car, a metallic green Pontiac Le Mans. I spent my weekends traveling up and back to Arrowhead, driving in style.

The free love - pot smoking - acid dropping-hippie days of the 1960s faded and morphed into the disco do the hustle bar scene, and I adapted along with it. Now, at 25, I attained a savoir-faire, less boy, more man.

To accommodate the shift in the 1970s attitude, Whitey updated Arrowhead. The hall that led to the bar and lounge, which the Zigg Zaggs painted black and wild DayGlo colors, was repainted a subdued tan. Instead of a live band, he hired a DJ to pump out canned dance music and added a mirrored spinning ball that hung in the lounge's center. One essential factor remained; there were always loads of girls looking for love.

Arriving on a Memorial Day weekend came the girls from Bayridge Brooklyn. They were a high-spirited gang of five disco frequenting girls that liked to party and have fun. For Arrowhead, they were a sorely needed shot of vitamin B-12 with a cup of espresso.

Marie, Diane, Annette, Jill, and Tina were close friends. All were attractive and worked as secretaries on Wall Street. When they entered the bar, everyone's head turned. Each wore the tightest fitting jeans, the new style 2.5-inch high platform shoes, and had a distinctive scent of "Charlie" by Revlon, the trendy perfume.

The new dance craze was the Hustle. No one at Arrowhead had ever heard of it or knew how to do it except the girls from Bayridge. When they danced with each other on Friday night, undulating to the DJ's music, it was an incredible moment. They were a group I had to meet.

"Hi, I'm Steve. That's an interesting dance you were doing. What is it?"

Sipping her drink through a straw, Annette replied, "The Hustle. Wanna learn?"

"Yes, I do."

She walked over to the DJ, quietly requested something, and *"Could It Be I'm Falling In Love,"* by the Spinners, played on the sound system. Annette sashayed back to the bar and pulled me aggressively to the dance floor.

"Now, watch, follow me, and don't ask questions," she directed.

I carefully paid attention to Annette's every move as she turned her feet and swayed her hips. She danced to the music with confidence and a fluid syncopation. It was a huge turn-on for me, and she knew it.

I was about to ask her a question when she said, "No questions, just watch."

Annette continued the lesson, and I paid close attention.

"You catch on quickly," Annette said.

"You're a good teacher," I replied.

As Annette and I walked back to the bar, Jill, Tina, Diane, and Marie, gathered around us to approve my newly acquired skill. One by one, they took turns dancing with me, and my ego swelled.

Of the bunch, Annette was the one that had my attention. But something didn't feel right, and a voice in my head whispered, "Steve, she's not interested."

At 1 AM, Marie loudly commanded, "OK, girls, it's time to head back to our rooms. We have to get up early and go riding."

Like baby chicks in a single file, they followed Marie out of the lounge, with Annette being the first in the line.

Early Saturday morning, Marie, Diane, Annette, Jill, and Tina gathered and waited for the first ride at the stables. Eddie, a riding instructor, saw them and drooled.

"Hey Steve, do you see what's outside ready to ride?"

Playing dumb, I replied, "No, what?"

"Look, Look."

"Oh, the girls from Bayridge. Yeah. I met them last night."

"You did

"Yeah. We partied and danced in the lounge."

Eddie went silent.

After brushing my horse, I came out of the stables and greeted them.

"Hey, girls. Now it's my turn to teach you."

Joey and Eddie helped me saddle-up the girls, including the rest of my novice ride. I positioned Annette behind me, then Jill, Tina, Diane, and finally, the mother hen, Marie. The other novice riders were last.

"OK, everyone, follow me," I shouted.

As we left, Joey - the stable foreman - quietly reminded me, "Stevie, I know you like them, but don't stay out for more than a half-hour."

"OK, Joey, I won't."

A quarter of the way into the trail, we paused at a place called the Rest Stop - a spot where riding instructors gave the Arrowhead lecture on riding safety, bragged about how macho they were, and tried to gain brownie points with a female guest they were trying to romance.

I made the obligatory safety sermon and then strolled over to Annette with my horse in tow.

"How do you like the horse I got you? Is she comfortable?"

"Yes," Annette said with a smile.

Her friends giggled at the attention I gave Annette, which made me suspicious. Why were they laughing? Did they know something I didn't?

We finished the first segment of the ride and headed back to the stables within my allotted time. Before we got back, I shouted to everyone, "Don't forget to tell the foreman how much you liked the ride."

I looked at Joey as we approached and tapped my watch to show my timeliness. He gave me a thumbs-up.

Early on Saturday night, I went to the lounge - hoping my efforts towards Annette worked - and waited for her and the gang to arrive. At 9:30, Marie, Diane, Annette, Jill, and Tina - laughing and chatting - burst into the lounge and greeted me.

"Hi, Steve," they all said in unison.

I practiced my new dancing skills - like I did on Friday evening - and talked about the new Brooklyn and Manhattan disco scene. All the girls were excellent company, but each time I danced with Annette and tried to get cozy with her, she would break away from me and dance by herself. Her message became clear. She wasn't interested in romance.

Tired and feeling a little foolish, I called it an evening and left the lounge. While walking back to my room, someone bumped me from behind, stuffed something in my back pocket, and whizzed past me. I looked to see who it was.

At first, I didn't recognizer her. But her face quickly became familiar. It was a female guest that was on a ride I had taken out on Saturday afternoon.

Astonished, I reached into my back pocket and pulled out a torn yellow piece of paper with *Phyllis* and a phone number written on it. I stopped, studied the note, then began to sing, *"If you're not with the one you love, love the one you're with."* Now, Annette's rejection had less sting.

Sunday afternoon, I loaded my Le Mans with my gear and headed back to Brooklyn when Diane came running towards me.

"Steve, can you give me a lift back to Brooklyn?"

"Yeah, where in Brooklyn?"

"Just off Ocean Parkway. You said you take Ocean Parkway back to your apartment?"

"Are you packed and ready to go, Diane?"

"Yep, my bags are in the lobby."

"Ok. Get your stuff. I'll wait for you in my car."

I was glad to have Diane's company on the long trip back to Brooklyn. We talked about many things, including Annette.

"I like Annette. What's her story, Diane?"

"She's got a boyfriend."

"Humm. That explains it."

"Do you think I should keep trying?"

"No, Steve, you're wasting your time."

We reached Ocean Parkway, and I dropped Diane at her house.

"Thanks, Steve. Hey, I made a reservation for next weekend and could use a lift. Are you going back up to Arrowhead? Can I call you?" Diane asked

"Yeah, I'll be there next weekend. Here's my number. Call me Thursday."

The girls from Bayridge became frequent weekend guests at Arrowhead, and Diane often traveled with me on my trip from Brooklyn to the Ranch. I danced and rode horses with all the girls, and we enjoyed each other's company. I tried to romance Annette several times, hoping she would change her mind about me, but Diane was right; it was a waste of my time. The sea was brimming with other fish, and my passion for her faded.

Throughout 1973 and 1974, my career as a photographer took precedence over Arrowhead. Working there became a low priority.

The horseback riding, 1000-acre trails, and good American cooking were still superb at Arrowhead, but the vibrant singles scene of the 60s and the zany anything-goes atmosphere was replaced with Moms, Dads, and kids. Whitey, too, had his fill of Arrowhead and sold it twice. The new owners were incompetent, and he had to take it back each time.

The Disco scene was on the rise during that period and made the Dude Ranch for singles passé. If I wanted to meet girls - and still did - making that punishing 3-hour trek was unnecessary. Love was now conveniently around the corner.

In Manhattan and the other four boroughs, Discos were popping up at a feverish pace everywhere. They were chockful with single girls looking for love, and I was there to assist.

Entered a Boy Exited a Man

By 1976 I was rarely at Arrowhead. Occasionally, I would spend the weekend - as a paying guest - with a girlfriend or alone to ride the trails and enjoy the fresh mountain scenery.

The people and excitement, which were attractive in the late 60s, were no longer alluring. Arrowhead had changed, and so did I.

It was a fascinating 8-year journey. I met all my goals and inadvertently achieved more.

Rubbing elbows with Arrowhead's strange mix of characters, working with Bernie, Mike, Pete, Whitey, Bobby, Paula, and the staff, taught me valuable life lessons. I acquired self-discipline and character. Most importantly, I entered a boy and exited a man.

Made in United States
North Haven, CT
27 June 2022

20673811R00093